the case for going to the moon

books by Neil P. Ruzic

THERE'S ADVENTURE IN METEOROLOGY

THERE'S ADVENTURE IN CIVIL ENGINEERING

STIMULUS (ED.)

THE CASE FOR GOING TO THE MOON

the case for going to the moon

By NEIL P. RUZIC

with a foreword by
Arthur C. Clarke

Published by special arrangement
with Industrial Research

G. P. PUTNAM'S SONS
New York

This book is dedicated to Gen. Georges F. Doriot, with whom I share a motto: "Why not?" And to my son, David, who asks only: "When?"

acknowledgments

THE CASE for going to the moon—and probably any similar speculative argument — could not have been made without the active cooperation of the many students of the moon and related sciences. These are the selenologists, geologists, astronomers, biologists, chemists, astrophysicists, meteorologists, engineers, economists, and others who so generously gave their time to talk and write to me about their specialties.

Of them all, I thank most prominently Dr. Harold L. Garbarino, of Electro-Netic Steel Inc., an Einstein-like versatilist who always takes the time wherever he is to ponder answers to scientific questions.

The other professional scientists who contributed the most include: Dr. Jack Green, North American Aviation Inc.; Arthur C. Clarke, the famous British science writer and novelist; Dr. A. Dauvillier, Pic-du-Midi Observatory, Collège de France; H. A. Steinherz and Dr. Milo P. Hnilicka, of National Research Corp.; Dr. Ralph B. Baldwin, Oliver Machinery Co.; Dr. Frank D. Drake and Dr. Thomas Gold, of Cornell University; Dr. Harrison Brown and Dr. Lee A. Du-Bridge, of California Institute of Technology; Dr. Sidney W. Fox and Dr. S. Fred Singer, of the University of Miami; Dr. Lloyd V. Berkner, Graduate Research Center of the Southwest; George J. Howick, Eldon Sneegas, Charlton Price, Howard Gadberry, John Loser, and Dr. Charles Kimball, all of Midwest Research Institute; Alvin N. Bird, Southern Research Institute; Howard Betts and Albert Siegel, of IIT Research Institute; Dr. John A. O'Keefe, Dr. Hugh L. Dryden, James E. Burnett, Dr. Cyril Ponnamperuma, Dr. Eugene Shoemaker, Breene M. Kerr, Joseph Burlock, and many others in the various NASA laboratories and offices; Dr. Harold C. Urey and Dr. Melvin Calvin, of the University of California; Dr. William H. Pickering and A. R. Hibbs, of the Jet Propulsion Laboratory; Dr. Gilbert V. Levin, Hazleton Laboratories Inc.; W. Randolph Lovelace, The Lovelace Foundation; Dr. Laurence W. Fredrick, Leander McCormick Observatory, University of Virginia; Dr. J. R. Killian, Massachusetts Institute of Technology; Arthur B. Francis, Varian Associates; George T. Spees, Warnecke Electron Tubes Inc.; Dr. J. Allen Hynek, Dearborn Observatory, Northwestern University; Richard Schlegel, Michigan State University; Dr. Lloyd A. Wood, Air Force Office of Scientific Research; W. J. Lange, Westinghouse Electric Corp.; Dr. T. Keith Glennan, Case Institute of Technology; Dr. R. E. Gibson, Applied Research Laboratory, The Johns Hopkins University; J. B. Kendrick, The Bunker-Ramo Corp.; Donald W. Male, Arnold Engineering Development Center; Lloyd G. Marts, University of Denver; Dr. Alex G. Smith, University of Florida; Dr. Jack DeMent, DeMent Laboratories; Dandridge M. Cole, General Electric Co.; Dr. Herbert Trotter, General Telephone & Electronics Laboratories Inc.; Dr. Cledo Brunetti, FMC Corp.; and Robert W. Prehoda, The Marquardt Corp.

In addition, I acknowledge the constructive criticisms of the members of the *Industrial Research* Editorial Advisory Board, especially those of Dr. Albert V.

Crewe, Argonne National Laboratory; Rear Adm. Rawson Bennett, Sangamo Electric Co.; Dr. Clyde E. Williams, Clyde Williams & Co.; and Dr. Harlow Shapley, Harvard University Observatory, as well as Arthur Clarke and H. A. Steinherz mentioned above.

I also express my appreciation for the many information-gathering chores performed by the following *Industrial Research* staff members: Jack D. Curley, Mrs. Sue Gibbons, Frank J. Granzeier, T. Frederic Sinclair, Dr. Victor J. Danilov, Carol A. Sampson, Mrs. Rebecca Heiner, and, especially, my wife, Mrs. Carol W. Ruzic.

n p r

contents

foreword

WHY GO TO THE MOON? In one sense, this question is unanswerable, for the more astringent philosophers have found no completely convincing reason for any human activity, including breathing. But once it is admitted that life *is* worth living and that it was not all a dreadful mistake to have left those cozy Pleistocene caves, the question takes another form. We will obviously, because we are men, go to the moon as soon as it is technically and economically feasible.

The technical feasibility is being established by the Apollo Project and its Russian equivalent. The economic feasibility (using the moon as a base for research, manufacturing, mining, observing, etc.) is the subject of this book.

I first "met" the author, Neil P. Ruzic, a decade ago by airmail between Colombo, Ceylon, and Beverly Shores, Indiana (two of the most distant and unlikely places on this planet for science writers) when he sent me a short story he'd had published in *Galaxy*, a science fiction magazine to which we both contributed.

He explained that he borrowed the future-science idea of the story from something I had written in a scientific journal. It was the freezing of human ova and spermatozoa and combining them some centuries hence in an incubator on a starship. In Ruzic's story, one of the resultant humans developed as an idiot and chose to land the spaceship on a star instead of on its earth-type planet.

The fact that the idea for freeze-preservation of sex cells did not originate with me is beside the point. The point is that the more Ruzic began to write science and the less he wrote science fiction, the more optimistic and imaginative he became. Later, in 1958, he started *Industrial Research* magazine for creative scientists and engineers, and it was I (and 70,000 others) who began to borrow the ideas from him!

Today, as the editor & publisher of the informative — and, incidentally, beautifully-produced — magazine *Industrial Research,* Neil Ruzic is in a unique position to survey the progress of modern technology, and to chart its future course.

Most books don't get the benefit of so many ideas and constructive criticisms prior to publication as "The Case for Going to the Moon." Before writing this book, Ruzic sent out detailed questionnaires to 7,800 of his readers and other scientists, and culled their opinions on the impact of space upon their specialties. Later, he sent out at least 50 copies of each chapter to selected scientists, and incorporated many of their comments in the manuscript. Still later, when the book appeared in monthly installments in *Industrial Research,* additional feedback was received from hundreds of some-times-pleased, sometimes-angered — but always stimulated — scientific readers.

If ever a book can grow, this one has grown and matured through the lengthy comments of many hundreds of scientists who want to go to the moon and other hundreds who do not.

Many of those who are against the moon project, or apathetic toward it, will be converted after reading this book. Yet there will remain critics who will deride the author's optimism and devotion to purpose. Others will find fault with his emphasis on the technically possible and his lack of acknowledgment of the technically impossible. I remind them that this book is called "The Case *for* Going to the Moon," not "The Pros and Cons of Going to the Moon," and that the technical obstacles have been so overemphasized elsewhere as to enshroud the entire program in a cloud of pessimism and apathy. Ruzic's book, like his magazine, fights for a cause in a day when all too many don't bother.

Despite the author's unusual persistence in weighing the words of literally hundreds of scientific experts, I suppose some critics will complain about technical inaccuracies (they always do in books of scientific speculation). Where they do, I suggest they re-examine their complaints and re-discover, as I have, the vast instances of scientific controversies that still exist. This book is technically accurate (today!) in discussing matters of fact. Its speculation, carefully labelled as such, emphasizes the many differences of scientific opinion that only prove the adage: the more we learn, the more we discover there is more to be learned.

"The Case for Going to the Moon" argues for learning, for hastening that first significant step into space because we will discover knowledge as well as useful things through the effort. Without recourse to mathematical formulae or unexplained scientific verbiage, the author leads you through new and not-yet-new developments in almost every branch of thought — physics, chemistry, geology, meteorology, astronomy, biology, engineering, sociology, economics, and even philosophy.

Yet for all that, this book is a practical one. It maintains that science and space travel should have a practical purpose. Because of this attitude (as opposed both to the pure science and the political approach), and because it is written in ordinary English, this book is for three classes of readers. First, it is for intelligent laymen who have wondered why we should spend all that money to go to the moon. Second, it is for statesmen attempting to divest their opinions about space from vested interests as they ponder why we should spend all that money to go to the moon. Third, it is for those scientists unashamed to admit we're all laymen in someone else's field as they contemplate why we should spend all that money to go to the moon.

I suspect that this book will be a revelation to a good many people in all three groups, especially those who talk about the "Moon Race" as if it were only that. (The fact that it *is* a race is perhaps its least important feature.) Some will be badly shaken by talk of large-scale lunar industrial operations, "lunar cryostats" and "mobile water mills" that the author has invented, the eventual colonization of the solar system, and communications with intelligent life elsewhere — yet today, refusal to face such possibilities is nothing less than a flight from reality. There is no excuse for it, in the second half of the 20th Century.

In the 1840s, Senator Daniel Webster informed the Congress of the United States that he would not vote one cent for the development of the West — as it was a howling wilderness that would never be of the slightest use to anybody. Time has a way of dealing with such arguments; so it will be in this case. Indeed, our grandchildren will find it quite inconceivable that a book such as this was ever necessary.

But it is, and Neil Ruzic is to be congratulated on writing it. I hope he is still around when it becomes time to produce the sequel: "The Case for Going to Alpha Centauri."

Arthur C. Clarke

Colombo, Ceylon
1965

preface

I AM UNEASY. I resent the passive attitudes many scientists have toward the challenge of science, especially their passivity concerning the greatest scientific, technological, and industrial opportunity of all time — the development of space — a challenge so limitless and exciting as ultimately to surpass all previous human accomplishment.

On the threshold of landing the first men on another world, I am angry that so many scientists do not voice the scientific benefits of the expedition to the moon, concerned that the industrial directors in charge of tomorrow are tranquil to the future, disturbed that our non-scientific Congress is unrealistic in its reasons for space appropriations, and disgusted with scientific journals that have abdicated their responsibilities of leadership and fail, even, to present a point of view.

Hundreds of important scientific and cold-cash reasons abound for going to the moon. Exploring them is the purpose of this book.

Neil P. Ruzic

Beverly Shores, Indiana
1965

"Speak what today thinks in words as hard as cannon balls, and tomorrow speak what tomorrow thinks in hard words again, even though it contradict everything you said today."

Ralph Waldo Emerson

Chapter **1**

cases against the moon

MANY PEOPLE — scientists as well as laymen — who discount the practical scientific and industrial uses of the moon are strangely convinced that spending $13-million every day on getting there is perfectly justified for reasons of national prestige!

Using the manned moon shot as a stunt to focus prestige on our already prestigious nation should concern the reader as little as it does me. Consistent, creative, and forceful decisions in Viet Nam, Cuba, and the Congo can buy more influence than a $20-billion moon trip. So can curing the common cold (or even cancer), running a successful Peace Corps, or exhibiting hydrogen bombs on holidays. Going to the moon *also* will contribute substantially to U.S. prestige, but not significantly more than other dramatic accomplishments on earth.

There are other reasons why we should *not* pursue the moon objective. We should not go there to develop a military base from which to dominate the earth. The moon is too distant for that. It is far simpler and much more accurate to fire ICBMs from one nation to another without going anywhere near the moon.

An equally ridiculous reason often given for conquering the moon is to solve the over-population problem. In the 1840s, the argument goes, the population of earth reached 1-billion. Less than a century later it was 2-billion. Only 30 years later it was 3-billion. Soon after we land men on the moon, in the next decade, it probably will increase to 4-billion. These facts are startling. The world population really is exploding and its control is probably the most critical problem facing mankind today.

Colonizing the moon, however, will do little to solve a population crisis of such magnitude. Ignore, if you can, the inherent environmental problems of maintaining millions of people on the airless moon, which is quite different than supporting several thousands of scientists and rocket engineers. Even so, the moon is too small and our populace too explosive to do much good. If the rate of our prolificacy does not decrease markedly, it will take only a few centuries to transform all the matter of the entire earth, moon, and planets into human flesh!

Viewing the development of the solar system as the mere beginning of a 100- or 1,000-year project for populating this and other entire galaxies is a different matter, of course. But I have the odd feeling that if the planets-for-colonization proponents really tried, they might think up easier solutions to the population plight — and better reasons for researching interstellar travel.

If the moon is not worth developing to bolster our national prestige, or as a base from which to throw bombs at the earth, or even as a substitute for birth control . . . then, what good is it?

As the great Scottish physicist James Clerk Maxwell once replied to that kind of question, "What good is a baby?"

This undeveloped child of the earth we call the moon is a goal, a treasury of information, and a desirable platform in space. Practical scientific, industrial, and humanitarian reasons for going to the moon include employing its unique environment for research and manufacturing; mining it for useful materials and significant geological knowledge; locating on it meteorological and astronomical observatories, hospitals, and biological laboratories; developing it as a space port from which to explore the solar system and the universe; and utilizing its byproduct to massively stimulate our economy and to help prevent war.

The chapters that follow will attempt to explain why these things are important and profitable. These cases for going to the moon — and beyond — will begin with early research considerations and proceed by gradual steps to the farthest-out of all space motives: finding extraterrestrial life.

But before describing the far-reaching applications of the moon, a digression into a series of recent surveys may shed light on scientists' diverse attitudes toward going to the moon.

Immediately prior to writing this book, seven different questionnaires were sent to seven different groups of scientists and engineers. In each case, 1,000 or more questionnaires were mailed. Returns from all these polls were low: meteorologists returned 14.8% of their specific-interest questionnaires; vacuum specialists 10.2%; astronomers 8.4%; geologists 8.3%; and biologists 6%. Chemists returned 21.4% and engineers 18.2%. Various professional society lists were used to reach all groups except the last two. These were selected at random from the *Industrial Research* magazine circulation rolls.

A definite lack of interest is evidenced by the average 12.6% return of the 7,742 questionnaires mailed. Even in a mail survey, a less than 15% return indicates decided disinterest in a subject. By contrast, *Industrial Research* mail surveys that we use to sample our readership on routine, commercial, subjects — such as what kind of microscope do you use? — rarely average a return of less than 30%.

Why was the interest so low?

About 100 non-respondents were telephoned at random to learn the reasons for their non-response. Most of them indicated they just didn't care. Either they hadn't thought much about it, they said, or they believed their own research projects, subjects taught, or professional interests were not sufficiently broad as to benefit from space research!

The remainder was divided almost equally into camps pro and con; thus, the seven mail surveys are probably a good measure of the attitudes of scientists and engineers throughout the nation *who are interested* one way or the other. Here is the tally of scientific apathy:

	FOR	AGAINST	DON'T CARE*
Respondents ..... (12.6%)	7.2%	5.3%	0.1%
Non-respondents .. (87.4)	11.1	10.9	65.4
All scientists/engrs. (100.0%)	18.3%	16.2%	65.5%

Includes those who are undecided.

Thus, while there are slightly more scientists for moon attainment than against it, pro and con groups alike are in the minority.

Of the 975 scientists and engineers who did respond, about a quarter indicated that they thought the moon program was of no scientific or practical use. Some quipped it was of no "earthly use" other than providing a supply of green cheese. In their more polite comments, this vocal quarter of respondents said it was a circus stunt designed to enhance U.S. prestige among the uncommitted and uninformed.

Another fifth of respondents (included in the "against" column above) felt the program was important, but that it was proceeding too fast and that the money could be spent better on oceanography or health research.

In other words, scientists and engineers today vote in significant minorities for going slow in the space venture, or in stopping it altogether. Here they join the apathetic 65% of the scientific community too engrossed in narrow specialties to see any benefits.

The attitude of apathy, starting with the scientists, has spread to Congress. Almost exactly three years from the day President Kennedy first proposed a manned assault on the moon, the space program on May 21, 1964, was caught in a snarl on the House floor. This first of several delays heralded a changing Congressional mood over urgency of the lunar expedition.

That year was an election year, and the manned moon program became — and remained — a ripe issue for political polarizationists. Those who would rename the Republican party Conservative and the Democratic party Liberal, point out that President Eisenhower used to oppose billions for the moon and that most Democrats are for them. In his acceptance speech for the Republican nomination, Senator Goldwater followed a long summary of national problems by gibing "This is a goal far, far more meaningful than a moon shot." And the *Chicago Tribune,* long-time foe of anything Democratic or non-Midwest, had this to say on June 29, 1964:

"Every year, more senators are coming around to the sensible opinion that while the moon is a lovely place to look at from a distance, it isn't worth spending more than $20-billion to visit ... Last year, Senator Lausche's (D-Ohio) proposal to cut $150-million from the bill then presented to the Senate drew 32 votes. And now at least 38 senators agree with Mr. Fulbright (D-Ark.) that the moon race is an extravagant example of 'haste and waste.' It is good to find both senators from Illinois on the side of common sense, as well as both from Wisconsin and Iowa."

According to the *Tribune*, only 34 Democrats and eight Republicans bothered to oppose the most recent cut, and "it is becoming increasingly clear that they are only protecting the administration from embarrassment and holding the pork barrel open to states which expect to benefit from space spending, such as Texas, New Mexico, Nevada, California, and several southern states."

The pork barrel criticism undoubtedly is at least partly true. As has happened so many times before, Congress is supporting a scientific project for non-scientific reasons: political patronage, and to achieve a victory in space that would establish the U.S. as Power No. 1 in the eyes of the rest of the world. When President Kennedy committed the nation to a $20-billion program of beating the Soviet Union to the moon, he did so after careful NASA evaluation of what possibly could be done to surpass the Russians in space. He chose the moon, and pushed it through Congress with unprecedented speed, not because he felt the moon itself had any special value, but because a manned moon landing offered the best chance for an important space triumph.

This kind of governmental support is precarious because it could reverse itself when the beat-the-Russian need, or mood, reverses itself (as it has temporarily), or after an election when a new party comes to power with different plans of patronage.

Improperly motivated governmental support for science happens because Congress, even today, is largely non-scientific. It will happen again and again until those who make the decisions go back to school or get elected from one.

Only 2.8% of members of the 88th Congress—three out of 100 senators and 12 out of 435 Congressmen—have scientific backgrounds, even including former pharmacists, physicians, a dentist, and a nurse. Yet, according to research biologist Dr. Joseph W. Still, scientists actually played a relatively more important role in the early affairs of our government when we were a weak agricultural nation than they do now. Of the men who signed the Declaration of Independence, for instance, 11% were scientists, almost four times the present record.

What does all this mean? First that Congress, consisting of few scientists and few statesmen, will not forever support billions for space when the scientists themselves don't much care. That the apathy toward the space program among those who can benefit from it the most, the scientists, is widespread. That the billions spent so far for space have bought their *disinterest*. That every newspaper, radio, and TV news program in the country romancing the blow-by-blow race to the moon have not fired the scientific imaginations of the majority of our scientists and engineers. That the thought, independent of dollars and publicity, of man in his millionth year at last stepping from his planet of origin has failed to awaken most scientific innovators in this country.

Apathy is one thing. Vehement opposition directed toward a budget conscious non-scientific Congress is another. Among the dozen distinguished scientists testifying before the Senate Committee on Aeronautical & Space Sciences in 1963, two influential leaders of scientists' thought — Dr. Philip Abelson, director of the geophysical laboratory, Carnegie Institution of Washington, and editor of the AAAS (American Association for the Advancement of Science) magazine *Science*, and Dr. Polykarp Kusch, Nobel prize-winning professor and chairman of physics, Columbia University — expressed themselves as generally against the space effort and specifically against landing a man on the moon in the early seventies.

Why? Because the projects are "not important." Abelson speaking:

"My comments will not be an official pronouncement of the organization, though they reflect what I believe to be the view of our readers." [*Science's* 91,620 readers are engaged primarily in life science research.] "As editor I am in touch with my audience . . . I have conducted an informal straw poll among scientists not connected by self-interest to NASA (National Aeronautics & Space Administration). The vote was 110 to three against the present manned lunar program. . . . Correspondence to the editor [is strongly against the program.] . . . The high magnification of the Palomar telescope brings the moon within the equivalent of a few hundred miles of earth. The moon has been weighed, its size is known, and the average density of its rocks determined. *We already know that there will be no objects of economic value to be brought back from the moon or any of the planets* [italics mine] . . .

"We know that the other parts of the solar system are intrinsically less habitable than the most miserable spot on earth. Life on the top of Mt. Everest would be sheer luxury in comparison with existence on the moon, or even on Mars, the most habitable of the planets," he testified.

Later, on Feb. 12, 1965, Abelson was quoted in the *New York Times* as saying he will go along with the moon program "provided that the public realizes it is chiefly for fun and adventure and not because some great contribution is being made to science."

At least Abelson and his magazine have the courage to present a point of view. Almost none of the 2,000 other scientific, industrial, or trade magazines in the United States, with the exception of those directly covering the aerospace field, has *anything* to say about whether we should go to space or how fast or why.

Paraphrasing more of Abelson's testimony, we find

that chances of finding extraterrestrial life are small; man is a poor scientific instrument; unmanned vehicles are doing the really important scientific work; the Apollo program is distorting scientific priorities by emphasizing a manned landing and therefore is slowing progress; diversion of talent to space is damaging to other sciences because we have a limited pool of geniuses, too many of whom are attracted to the "glamor" of space research; and the moon has been there a long time and will continue to be there a long time, so why hurry? And better we should work to cure cancer.

Senator Stephen M. Young (D-Ohio) concurs: "As one who has lost a wife of many years and also a son, due to cancer, I think I certainly go along with you, Dr. Abelson, that the encouragement of scientists to engage in research and try to conquer cancer — and then also mental illness — should not be sidetracked."

Now, at the risk of appearing anti-AAAS, anti-family, and anti-cancer/mental illness cures, I will patiently pick these premises to pieces.

The money we are spending and, hopefully, shall continue to spend in the indefinite future for the peaceful development of space is indeed a large sum — roughly $5-billion per year, or $13-million each day. Yet it is considerably less than the price of defense (almost $200-million per day), of alcoholic beverages (some $30-million per day), or of cigarettes and other tobacco products (about $22-million per day). If more funds are needed for cancer and health research, why take them from the space program?

Actually, the whole "let's-shift-funds" argument breaks down under scrutiny. The billions of dollars spent annually for various projects do not exist in some big stockpile in Washington waiting for us to channel them here and there. Even if we somehow could divert the millions for space to add to the millions already allocated for health, we soon would discover that new money in this area is not proportional to results.

Probably the cures of cancer and mental illness are applied science projects of great importance to mankind. But it is my contention that the pool of scientific genius is *not* limited, and that the great space effort *aids all scientific research* because of its tremendous byproduct of new knowledge. Obviously, the hundreds of NASA projects delve into almost every manner of scientific inquiry, from medicine to physics to psychology. As you read through this book, the enormity of the byproduct to be realized will become evident.

If a cure for cancer is found at about the same time men set foot on the moon, as the eminent cancer specialist Dr. Jacob Gershon-Cohen predicts, the similarity may not be entirely accidental. The cures for cancer, and mental illness, possibly could come about because some space scientist put to work on the toxicology of metabolites, or on studying the effects of plant growth under one-sixth gravity, or something, made a discovery of usefulness to cellular biochemists.

Certainly cancer research has not lacked funds. It has lacked only breakthroughs.

Whatever stimulates massive scientific activity in all disciplines will benefit all science, for what science mostly needs is a focal point that can command — because of that very "glamor" so derided — the attention, respect, and dollars of the world.

With 90% of all scientists ever born still alive and working today, with the rate of scientific and technological advancement accelerating now in geometric progression, the scientific world cries for a standard bearer, a stimulus, and a goal.

How better to achieve these breakthroughs in health and in other important fields than to batter the unknown on all scientific fronts. (Actually, Abelson's straw poll and my seven surveys show scientists to be *un*attracted to the space effort in spite of the glamor. My fear is that non-political benefits to be derived from development of the moon and solar system have not been glamorized nearly enough, that the careful sophistication so many scientists cultivate today is outweighing their normal tendencies toward curiosity and creativity that led them into science in the first place.)

As Thompson-Ramo-Wooldridge's Dr. Simon Ramo puts it, "A properly handled large space program, with a specific and (I will say quite unashamedly) *glamorous* center point of attraction, may have a long-run benefit in improving those processes that cause us to select and to educate the youngsters of today into the highly creative scientists and engineers of the future. The increased future supply may outweigh, in effect, any imbalanced deflection to space programs."

The Committee on Utilization of Scientific and Engineering Manpower — an outgrowth of President Kennedy's 1961 request for a review of the nation's technical manpower resources — has compared some government and industrial technical salaries. It reported on July 12, 1964, that "salaries paid to scientists and engineers at the upper levels of government career services are far below those prevailing at comparable levels in private industry."

How far? A top government scientist making $16,000 to $18,000 compared with a $20,000 to $30,000 a year man in industry; a $20,000 government man would earn $32,000 to $45,000 in private business for comparable scientific or technical management work.

The committee of 17 widely known technological leaders, headed by Dr. James R. Killian, recommended that before making major decisions — such as the lunar landing — the government should carefully assess the impact on the nation's technical manpower. But it said nothing in 153 pages to suggest that the space or moon program had diverted manpower from other fields.

Anyway, the latest figures show that NASA and all of the NASA contractors are employing 4% of our total supply of engineers and scientists. This leaves 96% of the total supply available for other uses. With profits in private enterprise at an all-time high, and higher in the non-space and non-defense companies than in those primarily government-financed for space, if those very profitable companies do not hire scientists and engineers, it is not because they can't get them. Their profit position gives them excellent bargaining power. Rather, failure to employ such scarce talents in large numbers is the result of cautious, conservative private entrepreneurs and has nothing to do with availability of personnel. Government-financed space R&D (research and development) is vigorously stimulating an increase in the number of highly trained scientists and engineers.

As for the moon continuing to be there for a long time, I can't quarrel, except to qualify "long time" by asking "for whom?" The moon will *not* be there for the asking for more than a very few years.

On Oct. 26, 1963, Premier Khrushchev — presumably concerned more with the problems of growing corn and importing wheat — suddenly declared that the Soviet Union would not race the United States to put a man on the moon.

A year and a half later, under a new premier, the flight of Voskhod II dispelled all doubts that lingered in this country about Soviet goals. When Voskhod passenger Lt. Col. Alexei Leonov became the first human to float in space on March 18, 1965, he did more than turn somersaults. He demonstrated that the Russians had developed capabilities directly applicable to landing men on the moon before we did. The fact that our Gemini IV repeated the experiment 77 days later (using a 25-foot cord instead of the 16-foot Soviet

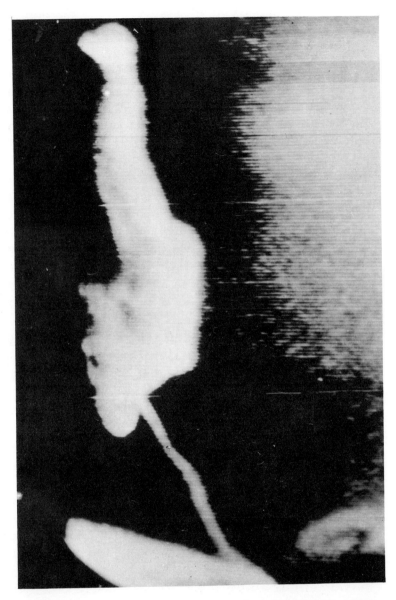

Cosmonaut Alexei Leonov floats 16 feet from Voskhod II, orbiting the earth on March 18, 1965, to become first man in space outside a spacecraft (for ten minutes). Following the achievement, Russians announced they were still very much in the race to land men on the moon. It will be a close race.

length) does not mean that the Russians are *only* 77 days ahead of us—any more than it means we are nine feet closer to the moon than they!

The apparent winner will shift many times before a man steps on the moon. Should the Russians appear to abandon the race in the future, remember what Vasily Seleznev, a top Soviet space official, said on the day of the historic Leonov flight:

"The target before us now is the moon, and we hope to reach it in no distant future."

If we fail to land on the moon as fast as our capability allows us, at least by 1970, the Russians surely will beat us. They may in any case.

If so, they could set up bases in strategic areas with very few men and easily prevent a U.S. landing. By claiming historical international precedent, such as Columbus invoked in planting the Spanish flag on the Americas, they could lay claim to the whole thing. Then any U.S. landing would be an act of aggression, on sovereign Soviet territory, and a belated Apollo could be shot down in self defense. Of course, we'd argue the point in the U.N.

The man-is-a-poor-instrument argument would make the cyberneticists among us laugh ... or cry in their perceptrons. Nobel laureate Dr. Harold C. Urey concedes that automated devices could collect preliminary data, but "only man, standing on the moon, can grasp the significance of its many and complex phenomena." Until the Evolutionary Cycle from Man to Machine* is completed, man continues to lumber along as the most imaginative, and cheapest, self-organizing system going.

Concerning the other arguments of the moon oppon-

*Arthur C. Clarke advocates in a Nov. 1961 Industrial Research article by this title that computers not only eventually will be able to replace man, but that they should. "No individual exists forever; why should we expect our species to be immortal? Man, said Nietzsche, is a rope stretched between the animal and the superhuman—a rope across the abyss. That will be a noble purpose to have served."

ents, I fail to see why "life on top of Mt. Everest would be sheer luxury in comparison with existence on the moon or Mars." Are we to send our astronauts there naked? Men will be considerably more comfortable in their controlled environment on the moon than they would be anywhere on earth, except possibly in an indoor swimming pool. Moreover, I despise the suggestion that luxury and comfort need flavor our decisions in space as they do so often in modern America and as they did so often in ancient Rome.

And . . . if "our chances of finding extraterrestrial life are small," I might add that they are infinitely smaller on earth than in space.

As far as "knowing that there will be no objects of economic value to be brought back from the moon or any of the planets," the crystal in my ball is not that clear. Anyway, why bring them back? The big problem, as we shall discuss later, is to get materials *to* the moon and planets. The efficient solution is to utilize what's there already. Every ounce of usable material, such as water, will be worth its weight in semiconductor-grade germanium at initial transportation costs of several thousand dollars a pound.

Astronomers quarrel with the high-magnification-of-the-Mt.-Palomar-telescope concept "bringing the moon within the equivalent of a few hundred miles of earth." Magnification is not the problem. The resolving power of the lens and mirror impeded by our ocean of atmosphere is the problem. Small "windows" into space for radio telescopy is a greater problem. As will be seen in Chapter VI, astronomers have substantially more to do than look at the moon (a job mostly taken over by amateurs).

The moon is useful because it happens, among other things, to be a steady base on which to mount an optical telescope unhindered by atmosphere, as well as a massive shield between a radio telescope positioned on the "far" side and thousands of disc jockeys.

Probably the best argument for the NASA program is the building of a space capability, with the moon as a goal that just happens to be nearby. NASA administrator James E. Webb likens Gemini to the old DC-3 aircraft, a beginning short-range workhorse designed to move men and materials, and the Apollo to the 707, a highly sophisticated long-range vehicle. The fact that Gemini-to-Apollo is measured in months, whereas the DC-3-to-707 was a matter of years, underscores the rapid pace of our technological advance.

The arguments above briefly answer the objections of those who fail to find reasons for going to the moon, but any mere tally of condensed arguments for the moon cannot much hope to improve the focus of the myopic. The problem lies in the brevity of most pro-Apollo arguments. There is no *one* good reason to go to the moon; rather, there are hundreds of good technical and other reasons. The sum of all of them provides overwhelming acclamation for making the trip, and therefore makes it necessary to explore each of the reasons in some detail.

Keep in mind that it takes less work and is more comfortable to be against something than for something. It is always easier to be a keeper of the status quo, for the keeper's arguments give the impression of being stable, conservatively sensible. The phrase, "down-to-earth," for the keeper, is a challenge.

Dr. T. Keith Glennan, NASA's first administrator, and now president of Case Institute of Technology, tells the story of an old riverboat pilot who complained to Mark Twain about the change from sail to steam. The old pilot wanted no part of the newfangled steam contraptions. "Maybe so," replied Twain, "but when it's steamboat time, you steam."

Today is spaceship time, Mr. Keeper, and when it's spaceship time, you space.

Chapter **2**

WITNESS:

WHEREAS, a 15-million square mile world orbits the earth only 238,866 miles away (mean distance); and

WHEREAS, the landing of men and instruments upon this world is within the present capability of the United States; and

WHEREAS, the entire surface of this new-old world exists in an almost perfect vacuum, with temperature extremes of from −270 F to 260 F each lunar day, allowing for unique scientific experiments;

NOW, THEREFORE, the following arguments are detailed in the interests of performing research in vacuum and in the extreme temperatures on the surface of the moon.

(TIME ESTIMATE for beginning vacuum research on the moon: 1972.)

the case for research in the lunar vacuum

THE MOON is an arid, airless world, devoid of wind or rain, lakes or oceans. It is cloudless, soundless, totally desolate. These qualities are among its scientific assets.

In order to discuss the opportunities for doing significant scientific research on the moon, it is necessary first to explain vacuum and its modern unit of measurement, the *torr*, named after Evangelista Torricelli, Galileo's assistant who invented the barometer in 1643.

Devising an experiment to prove Galileo's theory that air had weight, Torricelli filled a glass tube with mercury, inverted it, and placed the open end in a bowl of the same liquid. If air had weight, it would push against the mercury in the vessel and force the mercury to rise in the tube.

Air does have weight, of course, and this atmospheric pressure forced the mercury to climb about 30 inches; thus the atmosphere weighed "30 inches of mercury." One day, as a storm approached Florence, the mercury in Torricelli's tube dropped more than an inch. As the storm began to subside, the mercury rose again.

Torricelli realized that the pressure of the atmosphere changes, heralding storms. Thus he discovered both the principle of the barometer and the measurement of "vacuum," which is considered to be any pressure less than atmospheric pressure.

Until recently vacuum was measured in inches or centimeters of mercury, but now modern vacuum technologists express low pressures in torr, an absolute unit. One torr is equal to 1/760 of a standard atmosphere. Therefore, normal atmospheric pressure is expressed as 760 torr. The pressure in a typical vacuum tube is about a millionth of a torr. This is written "0.000001 torr," or "1 x 10 to the minus 6th power," or simply "10^{-6}."

Vacuum technology is associated closely with space exploration. The following table shows the degree of vacuum encountered at various heights above the earth's surface:

HEIGHT IN MILES	PRESSURE IN TORR
Sea level	760 (or 7.6×10^2)
10	10^2
100	10^{-5}
1,000	10^{-11}
Probable vacuum at surface of moon	10^{-14}
Interplanetary space	10^{-16}

Measuring vacuum is easy (up to a point), but producing extreme ones is difficult. Here is our recipe for vacuum on earth:

Take a small chamber, pump as much air out of it as you can in a couple of days. Let cool with liquid helium to near absolute zero, condense out most of the remaining molecules. Place the entire chamber inside another chamber to protect against leakage, evacuating most of the air from between the walls. Inside the inner chamber, grind high-purity stainless steel walls to a mirror-smooth finish to minimize molecular out-gassing. Charge any remaining air molecules plus and the chamber walls minus, thereby trapping any lingering ions on the walls with a thin layer of titanium.

Result: 10^{-15} or maybe $^{-16}$ torr (even mass spectrometers cannot measure below 10^{-14} torr). The vacuum achieved is so hard that a molecule would travel an average of 30-million miles before colliding with another molecule.

Problem: The usable area, inside the chamber within a chamber within the coils of liquid helium, is about 18 inches in diameter and only 3 feet long. And expensive. And cumbersome, complex, time-consuming, and unwieldy.

The highly sophisticated little corner of interplanetary environment described above, while within our reach without leaving the earth, requires extremely careful engineering. The toll of time and equipment required to scale up to large chambers capable of system-level testing are staggering. Just the refrigeration cost of liquefying helium to simulate typical lunar vacuum in a "huge" 6- by 10-foot chamber is upwards of $20,000 for a ten-hour run.

No wonder far-sighted vacuum specialists covet the 15-million square miles of hard nothing on the moon. Although we cannot justify travel to the moon solely for vacuum research, it does present one of the important reasons for going, and it is not too early now to consider what we would do in this vast vacuum chamber with its floor almost the size of both American continents.

To help answer this question, a three-page questionnaire tailored to the vacuum uses of the moon was sent to the 1,742 members of the American Vacuum Society. They were asked to visualize a laboratory, or factory, on the moon where men work in virtually unlimited hard vacuum, protected either by space suits or inside a pressurized building. Assuming the problems of transportation to and from earth were solved in a reasonably economical manner (this salient assumption will be discussed in the next chapter), do you think such a moon facility would be worthwhile for your work?

Eliminating the manufacturers of vacuum chambers who thought they would be put out of business by such a facility, but including those who would supply "man chambers" and other equipment for the enterprise, about half (48%) of the 188 respondents answered yes. Why?

A typical response: "With unlimited high vacuum available, machines could be a lot simpler. Many, many more experiments could be tried. Experiments now requiring days could be done in a matter of hours, even minutes. One can visualize a tremendous development of experimental work on the moon, which could grow into production. One might be successful in rapidly producing devices on the moon that are next to impossible to make on earth due to high requirements for vacuum. It may well develop that these expensive devices would pay for the establishment of a high vacuum industry on the moon."

The thought of all the 10^{-14} nothing you want cannot help but seduce imaginative vacuum experimentalists. The production of test vacuums on earth now consumes an overwhelming percentage of researchers' energies. Mechanical difficulties such as leakage caused by faulty seals, inadequate ability of pumping systems to handle outgassing (the process of gas escaping, or "evolving," from a material exposed in a vacuum; the outgassing, of course, partially ruins, or "softens," the vacuum), heat dissipation, lack of adequate room for mechanical components — all of these complexities would be eliminated on the moon.

"How ideal to remove those confounded steel walls

One of the largest vacuum chambers ever built, this six-story space environment simulator at NASA's Goddard Space Flight Center tests entire spacecraft. Space simulation on the moon would be less cumbersome.

between me and my work," said one investigator. Another: "On the moon, things would be so simple there would be hardly any need for complicated equipment. Adhesion of the material being deposited would be strong and instantaneous; the brilliance and purity of the deposit would be beyond anything that could be attained in a confined chamber on earth."

What research projects would be significantly advanced if the work could be done in the unlimited near-perfect vacuum, extreme cold, or low gravity of the moon?

The answers to that question are ranked below; percentages of AVS respondents who are in favor of each type of research are shown parenthetically. Because someone is paying for this research today, the 23 reasons below represent a rank order of applied vacuum research of practical importance now. The thought that significant percentages of the physicists, chemists, biologists, and others doing vacuum research feel it could be done better on the moon is compelling.

The first dozen reasons will be explored in some detail. (The non-technical reader may wish to bypass these 12 examples; the remainder of the book is of more general interest.)

1 *Materials research* (75%) could be carried on in an uncontaminated, unbounded high vacuum environment, under either refrigerated or heated conditions for long periods of time. It would be necessary only to go outside the laboratory to introduce heat into an experiment.

To increase heat beyond the 260 F daytime ambient temperature, a solar furnace could be set up easily; it would be more effective on the moon since it would focus the sun's rays unhindered by atmosphere.

The materials barrier is the foremost technological problem of our time. Interplanetary flight, thermonuclear power, lightweight structures, corrosion-free implements, reliable electronics, all advanced technology is dependent upon the researcher's success in improving the properties of materials. Any experiment in which an ultra-clean surface is desirable (and in what materials experiment is it not?) could be conducted better in a lunar research facility where vacuum conditions exist naturally.

For instance, metals and semiconductors now are cleaned on an atomic scale by heating them in a vacuum chamber — a terribly restricted and expensive place, as has been explained. Why not simply leave them alone for a little while on the moon in the 260 F sunlight to accomplish the same thing?

An ultra-clean surface is desirable also in studying the force of friction, a little-known phenomenon according to H. A. Steinherz, director of engineering at NRC Equipment Corp., who has been producing ultra-high vacuums for many years. True friction between clean surfaces has been measured for only a few metals. Standard textbook figures refer to surfaces contaminated (actually lubricated) by adsorbed gas layers, since this is the way they normally are found on earth.

Gases adsorbed on the surface of a material affect it in many other ways too. The emission of electrons from a solid surface is sensitive to surface contamination, and electrical properties of semiconductors are strongly affected by adsorbed gas. Then too, the process of adsorption itself on large and varied surfaces could be observed easily in "slow motion" in the ultra-high vacuum of the moon.

The wonderful thing about doing materials research in an unusual environment is that unusual things happen. Graphite, a good lubricant at earth-normal pressures, actually becomes an *abrasive* below 10^{-6} torr. The transfer of heat, the flow of fluids, the insulating capacity of insulators, the behavior of dielectrics (nonconductors or insulators of electricity), and many other phenomena change considerably in vacuum.

True scientists, that is, those who thirst for knowledge, cannot help but wonder what would happen if their terrestrial experiments could be transferred to the moon.

2 *Thin film technology* (51.5%), a branch of microelectronics, refers to devices made from extremely thin layers of materials deposited on a base, or substrate, in a vacuum. Such thin films are beginning to be used widely in circuitry and computers because they are small and therefore respond instantly to minute changes in current. "Two-dimensional circuits," consisting of tiny terminals, interconnections, capacitors, and resistors, are formed by depositing a thin film of various materials on the substrate. Microsize active components then can be inserted separately to complete the circuit. Thin films of magnetic materials deposited on a nonmagnetic base also can be used to make memory storage devices for computers.

Vacuum, of course, is essential to thin film technology — the "harder" (more perfect) the vacuum, and the more of it, the better. Thin film research and testing could be undertaken on the moon on a massive scale without contamination from residual gas molecules. Now, when deposition of the film takes place in a vacuum chamber, residual gases in the system often affect the magnetic properties of thin films. Complex, expensive, and enormously tedious vacuum procedures have to be followed, not only to minimize the effect of random outgassing, but also to be able to test the samples without removing them from the chamber!

Thin film investigators today spend appreciably more of their time worrying about the vacuum than the research. Being able to work on the moon could be as great a boon to thin film technology as the advent of computers has been to data processing.

"Doping," or introducing small amounts of gases into the vacuum, could be done on the moon with precise control. Small amounts of oxygen, nitrogen, water vapor, or other gases (which we would collect as a byproduct of metallurgical research) could be intentionally bled into a simple closed chamber on the moon.

Whole books could be written (and I am sure they will be after 1970) about the research and production potential of thin films produced in the unlimited hard vacuum of the moon. Two examples will suffice here:

■ *Thin ferromagnetic films* made by vacuum deposition already are finding applications as memory elements and magnetic tapes for computers. The thin film components are similar in overall size to conventional ferromagnetic cores, or ferrites. These are cores made from iron and other oxides, usually shaped like doughnuts. They are used in circuits and magnetic memories because they can be magnetized and demagnetized very rapidly.

The advantage of thin ferromagnetic films over ferrites for these uses is that switching speed for the films is about 25 times greater than for the ferrites. Also important, film components can be operated above 390 F, while ferrite cores are not usable above 210 F.

■ *Tantalum thin films* — if they could be produced in quantity such as the moon environment allows — would find unique use in superconducting devices. Superconductors are metals and other materials that exhibit an abrupt decrease in electrical resistance as their temperature is reduced to the superconductive, or "transition," temperature near absolute zero. Absolute zero, about −460 F, is the theoretical lowest possible temperature. At the transition temperature, which varies with different superconductive materials, the resistance of the superconductor is practically zero.

Tantalum and several other metals are especially advantageous as superconducting thin films because they are highly resistant to corrosion and, more important, because they start out with a *high* electrical resistance at normal temperatures. A tantalum thin film would act as an efficient switch, for instance in a computer, as the temperature is increased or decreased above or below the transition temperature.

A good reason for performing tantalum thin film research on the moon is that a freshly deposited tantalum film is the greatest of "getters;" that is, it rapidly becomes contaminated by sorption (taking up of gas either by absorption or adsorption) of large quantities of residual gases in the vacuum system. For instance, if a film of 99.99% purity is required — which is impossible to obtain on a continuous basis in any terrestrial vacuum chamber — 9,999 tantalum atoms must strike the substrate for every residual gas atom that strikes it. The wide-open "vacuum system" of the moon, of course, eliminates the problem completely.

Now it has been pointed out by some who answered the vacuum questionnaire negatively that "cathodic sputtering" could replace the necessity for high vacuum in both examples above. Sputtering is an old method for producing refractory metal films. An electrical discharge is passed between two electrodes in inert gas at slightly low pressure. The cathode, fabricated from the material to be deposited, slowly disintegrates under bombardment of ionized gas molecules and some of the liberated material is condensed onto the sample.

But, while sputtering removes the necessity for high vacuum to achieve emission, vacuum still is needed to get rid of the undesirable residual gases before admitting the pure inert gas.

I have deliberately dwelt in detail on the problems of one area of research, that can be done better on the moon, to make a point. It hardly would be argued that cathodic sputtering is the preferred path of research to follow in the making of refractory thin films, to the exclusion of methods requiring continuous high vacuum, *if* we had a laboratory on the moon. Because we do not, the method has been presented by those who can see no reason for going to the moon *as a reason for not going!*

By way of historical precedent, it became painfully obvious in 1903 that aero-plane research was stymied because of the poor quality of components: bad engines, terrible strength-to-weight ratios in the structures, poorly guessed-at airfoils. The solution strongly advocated by the majority at the time was to forget about trying to plane through the air, as a boat does through water, and work instead toward development of dirigibles.

Santayana's maxim bears repeating here: "Those who cannot remember the past are condemned to repeat it."

3 *Metallurgy research* (48.4%) generally would benefit from an investigator's unlimited ability to maintain vacuum in purification studies. Pure metals could be created with maximum densities.

Thoroughly outgassed metals of greater than conventional purity and strength, pure grown crystals, and improved insulation materials would result from research on the moon.

The thought that refractory metals could be worked on standard metal-working equipment should intrigue any metallurgist who has considered the problem of how to operate a rolling mill in a 2 x 3-foot vacuum chamber.

Actually, some processes *not now feasible* could be carried out. For instance, refining of metal ores by heat alone, and without the use of a contaminating

Two pieces of copper held 0.03 of an inch apart in the enlarged picture above, taken through a tiny window in a National Research Corp. vacuum chamber, blend into each other and become one, below, when pressed together in a vacuum. Cold or "self" welding probably will be used in the 1980s for manufacturing spacecraft on the moon of local materials.

reducing agent, would work on the moon, but not on earth. Copper, nickel, and iron — elements almost sure to exist on the moon — could be reduced by this method. The oxygen byproduct could be collected easily and used for, among other things, life support of moon-based personnel.

4 *Welding research* (36.1%) in the absence of an oxidizing or contaminating atmosphere would be advanced abundantly. Cold or "self" welding — the joining of perfectly clean metals in vacuum without heat — could well be employed in the 1980s for manufacturing spacecraft on the moon using lunar materials. (The low gravity and lack of atmosphere, of course, make the moon our ideal Cape Kennedy, since vehicles could be launched to the earth or other planets with relatively low power requirements.)

Electron-beaming has welded complete complex configurations successfully without cracks or leaks. But a high degree of vacuum is necessary so that the electrons do not collide with gas molecules, which otherwise would become ionized and reduce the beam energy.

On earth, the use of high-vacuum chambers for electron-beam processing is practical only for small specialized parts, and not for large structures. When parts are too large to fit in a standard vacuum chamber, the chamber now must be *designed* to fit over the part before it can be evacuated!

Coating, conductivity, and other materials research also must be done to learn how to prevent metals — for instance in the contacts of a switch — from welding *un*intentionally. There is hardly a better place for simulating the moon than on its surface!

5 *Coating applications* (29%) have such an extensive future on the moon and coatings will be needed in such great quantity that they will be discussed in the chapter on lunar manufacturing.

Suffice it to say now that research on vacuum coatings has a future beyond development of mere decorative coatings, and that the stimulus to this potential will be provided by lunar needs. Research on industrial coatings for corrosion protection, coating lenses with silicon monoxide as well as the more conventional magnesium fluoride to decrease light loss, and coating electronic components for a variety of reasons will be done on the moon as a natural outgrowth of a production facility established to coat large sheets for lunar structures.

6 *Spectroscopic studies* (26.5%) would utilize the lunar vacuum to eliminate surface effects.

While the analysis of materials by emission spectroscopy usually is limited to metallic elements, nonmetallic elements such as carbon, sulfur, and phosphorus, also emit spectra when suitable activating sources are used. Because their spectral content (radiation) is more readily interpreted in the ultraviolet region of the spectrum, vacuum sources often are used to avoid dust and other contaminants found in the air.

Thus the moon once again becomes an ideal environment for science, in this case permitting ultimate sensitivity in what is probably our best qualitative/ quantitative tool for studying the atomic structure of substances found on the moon.

Also, since the moon is a stable platform not handicapped by dense atmosphere and magnetic fields, it is the best place from which to make solar and astronomical physical measurements of the solar corona and ultraviolet radiation, stellar radiation, gravitational deflection, and low-intensity stellar mapping. The advantages of such studies will be explored later, but let it be said here that a world without air is more of a scientific asset than a liability.

7 *Vacuum distillation* (26.5%) could be employed on the moon for a variety of research purposes such as investigations into refining superlubricants, as well as the obvious uses of turning urine or lunar ice into drinking water (and making "moonshine").

The moon is a natural-born still. The vacuum prevents residual gases in the still from affecting the distillation process. And the very high ambient temperature of the moon in sunlight is ideal for "degassing" liquids and for operating the evaporator.

"Degassing" is purposeful outgassing, or removal of sorbed and occluded gas from a material. Degassing usually is accomplished on earth by applying heat in a hard vacuum until the rate of evolution of gas decreases to a negligible value.

While the natural vacuum and daytime heat of the moon are ideal for degassing and evaporating, there will be a problem in condensing the steam or other volatiles. But to avoid the necessity for artificial refrigeration, these might be stored in a pressure vessel until nightfall when the temperature gradually falls to −270 F. A better solution would be to mobilize the still and cross into night for condensation and day for evaporation; this method will be explained more fully in the next chapter.

If you wonder why a simple shade or umbrella would not suffice to reduce temperatures drastically during the lunar day, it is because the surface of the moon, its rocks and mountains, and the shade itself reradiate the sun's heat. Even though convection (transfer of heat by a gas — the air on earth) is absent on the moon, we must contend with radiation, a more effective mechanism of heat transfer, which proceeds unhindered in vacuum.

The description sometimes portrayed of a glass of steam in the lunar sun turning to ice when the astronaut steps behind a boulder is inaccurate. Moving into shade on a typical summer day on earth might reduce the temperature from 90 F to 70 F (remember that the umbrella or the tree becomes a re-radiator). Doing the same on the moon might reduce the temperature from 260 F to about 180 F (the lack of conductive air will contribute somewhat, but only somewhat). Thus, a simple shade on the daytime moon probably would suffice to condense steam into water at 212 F, but would be insufficient for condensing many other fluids or for freezing them. The problem is different than on an artificial satellite where few objects are present to become re-radiators.

8 *Electron tube research* (23.2%) is another natural for the moon. Tube design is still primarily an empirical activity, where two major problems exist (on earth): contamination and geometry of the parts of the tube. Both are solved in the unbounded vacuum of the moon — contamination because there is literally nothing to interfere with the movement of electrons, and geometry because the elements can be moved or replaced at will and the results noted immediately.

As in all research endeavor, there is a tremendous advantage in getting immediate answers. On the moon, decisions can be made at once concerning proper cathode to anode spacing, or the distance in a cathode ray tube from emitter to target.

Moreover, because the moon's vacuum is unlimited, there is absolutely no problem in continuously maintaining or reproducing the vacuum, and, of course, no need to introduce gettering materials.

In fact, there is no reason why tubes *designed for lunar use* even need to have envelopes, unless they are simple shades (if a cave location is not practical) to keep them cool or to shelter them.

Nude, super-power tubes on the moon for radar and moon-earth or moon-spacecraft communications are not really fantastic. What is fantastic is the fact that the giant, 2 x 10-foot klystrons* used in the Ballistics Early Missile Warning System have been researched, produced, and operated on earth!

9 *Superconductivity* (23.2%), as has been partially explained, is an abnormally high electrical conductivity appearing quite abruptly in niobium, magnesium, zinc, lead, tin, cadmium, some other metals, and many alloys when cooled through a very low transition temperature near absolute zero.

It is important to realize that the most remarkable, and potentially most useful, aspect of the phenomenon is the apparent zero resistance to flow of a current in a superconducting circuit. In fact, currents have been started inductively by cooling a metal in a magnetic field and then withdrawing the field — to find the current seemingly continuing to flow indefinitely!

The absence of humidity on the moon, in addition to its low night temperature, becomes an asset for superconductivity research at cryogenic temperatures, especially for those experiments requiring long periods of time and large areas.

Temperatures, of course, are not "very cryogenic" on the moon, even at night. While the word "cryogenic" is used liberally, scientists usually apply it to temperatures below 80 K and use "ultra-cryogenic" from zero K to a few degrees above that. (The "K" stands for Kelvin, or the absolute scale.)

Night temperatures on the moon don't get much

Like an ordinary radio vacuum tube, a klystron generates or amplifies radio signals, but does so at microwave frequencies. Microwaves are radio waves that oscillate at frequencies around 10-billion cycles per second. They can be formed into a sharp beam like a searchlight. Radar systems such as the BEMWS in Canada, referred to above, send out beams of microwaves. If the beam strikes an aircraft or missile, it bounces off and returns to the radar set where it is recorded.

One of the largest cryogenics chambers ever built, this 11-foot diameter by 21-foot long Republic Aviation cooling shroud fits within a vacuum chamber in the laboratory. It reduces temperatures to about 80 K (320 F).

below about 105 K (−270 F) because of the enormous re-radiating power of the moon's 81-quintillion-ton mass. Temperatures deep in caves or crevices that have not seen sunlight for millions of years actually would be *higher,* not lower, because of the normal thermal gradient of the moon or radioactivity of wall rocks.

But by the use of a simple, inexpensive device, lunar temperatures can be brought to superconducting temperatures, without the expenditure of energy or unwieldy use of helium. This simple "lunar cryostat" will be described in the next chapter since it, and other easy inventions, are necessary before the moon can be considered seriously as a cryogenic manufacturing site.

10 *Conduction at low temperature* (19.4%) is an area of research where the lunar environment again would contribute to knowledge. The mechanism of thermal conduction is not completely understood. Molecules and electrons move differently at different temperatures in a conductor, semiconductor, and insulator.

On the moon, large-scale heat transfer experiments could be undertaken readily and more simply. For instance, the operation of large generators, transformers, motors, and entire systems could be studied in vastly different temperature extremes.

The study of conductivity — or any of the research projects suggested here — is not sufficient reason for going to the moon. But they are among the hundreds of reasons — extending, as shall be unfolded throughout this book, into astronomy, biology, geology, chemistry, and many other sciences and engineering activities beyond vacuum physics.

Cryobiology (17.4%) research on the moon should be tempting fare, particularly for basic researchers in microbiology. They would want to introduce many organisms to the moon, such as algae, if these hardy, colorful microplants have not already preceded them. Algae are extremely widespread on earth, living in nearly all environments including hot springs and polar ice caps. Some even grow in the dark. If anything can live naturally in lunar crevices, it may be something like algae.

The recent discovery of natural and mutant bacteria that are capable of accumulating enormous amounts of free amino acids in their culture medium; the fact that edible microorganisms rich in protein, B vitamins, and essential amino acids can be produced economically from petroleum, of all things; the discovery of an iron-based soil microbe called ferredoxin that functions as an electron-mediating catalyst for the biological production or utilization of hydrogen gas by bacteria; the knowledge that green and purple sulfur bacteria grow photosynthetically in the complete absence of oxygen ... and literally hundreds of other microbiological phenomena could be investigated unusually, with the likelihood of unusual results, under the unusual conditions of gravity and temperature of the moon. Again the limitless vacuum chamber beckons, offering an isolation-type laboratory for such pure research and providing easily for quick freezing of massive biological specimens.

While some of this basic research one day could result in radically economical methods of filling our lunarians' stomachs, applied research into freeze-drying probably could do that job almost immediately. Food will have to be grown indoors on the moon, and preservation will be necessary even in the early development of that world as the population of astronauts and scientists changes.

Freeze-drying, or dehydrating frozen food by sublimating its ice in vacuum, is cheaper and simpler than gamma and beta irradiation. And food so preserved tastes better. On earth, the presence of infinitesimal amounts of water in freeze-drying experiments cause food to deteriorate under long-term storage, a problem completely eliminated on the arid, airless moon.

Moon pessimists (who resemble Queen Isabella's advisors, more interested in how much gold could be taken from the Indies than in their development) may be placated with this thought: original work in vacuum drying at low temperatures not easily achievable in large areas on earth might well be expected to develop from lunar research. And research truly impossible on earth— such as that directed toward the effects of one-sixth gravity on plant growth—might bear fruit digestable not only by lunar explorers but also by the teeming tax-paying masses back home.

12 *Microminiaturization* (14.8%) of mechanical and electronic components the size of a pinhead, and whole circuits not much larger, could proceed at a faster, easier research pace on the moon (under a simple micrometeoroid shield to prevent agitation of moon dust).

Freshly showered women, masked like surgeons and clothed in lintless caps and gowns, now are commonplace in miniature bearing shops. A beam of sunlight can get a microbearing out of round; a globule of water can rust a dozen of them; the tiniest speck of dust is a roaring train to components measured in microns.

Probably only the moon's uncontaminated "atmosphere" can meet the molectronics engineer's requirement. A "molectronics," or "molecular electronics," engineer tailors the molecular properties of matter to perform electronic jobs, such as amplification. Complete audio amplifiers have been made into a space of about 1/500 of a cubic inch! The day will come, suggested Jack DeMent, president of the Portland, Ore. laboratories that bear his name, when we will build circuits by placing crystals of substance between the 30,000 lines to the inch of diffraction gratings and in micron-diameter holes of micropore filters.

Dr. Cledo Brunetti, of FMC Corp., who originated the term "microminiaturization" in 1957, feels one of the best of all miniaturizers is "the human body: a 10-cycle closed-loop sensing, computing, and performance system in a 0.1-ton chassis with a 0.1-horsepower motor."

We have a long way to go. Merely to duplicate the vision of discrimination of the human eye now would require an instrument as large as 10,000 times the volume as the few cubic inches employed in our bodies.

If we ever approach that duplication, we may well do it on the moon — not merely because the "atmosphere" is clean, but because it is virtually absent. Low gravity may help, but vacuum as well as cryogenic temperatures are needed — in large, reproducible areas — to coax molecules into behaving like amplifiers or oscillators. Breakthroughs in that realm may *depend* upon a lunar laboratory. Yet, even in the considerably less-sophisticated science of integrated circuitry (several years old by now!), vacuum enters as the ideal environment for deposition of the resistors, capacitors, and all interconnections.

The dozen examples above demonstrate at some length the vast research potential of our natural satellite, all stemming from one fact: the moon is small. It is, therefore, low in gravitational power, cannot retain an atmosphere, and loses most of its heat each night. Briefly completing the list offered in the questionnaire for ranking by the nation's vacuum specialists, we find:

Photoconductivity at low temperatures was chosen by 11% of AVS respondents as likely to benefit from lunar research. Radiation detectors in the infrared region are deposited in high vacuum, using lead sulfide or lead selenide. Visible light detectors, such as cadmium sulfide and cadmium selenide, also can be made by vacuum deposition. And gold films are vacuum deposited on organic films to make bolometers that detect radiation of wavelengths longer than 10 microns.

Optical properties of semiconductors should benefit from research in the lunar lab, say 9.7%. These researchers want to examine semiconductors not only at low temperatures and in clean, low atmosphere, but on a base where the terrestrial atmospheric shortcomings of solar simulation techniques can be overcome.

Magnetic resonance research, where radio frequency and magnetic fields are applied to a sample, often are conducted at very low temperatures to see what happens, and ought to be performed on the moon according to 8.4%.

Cyclotrons and other particle accelerators might be built on the moon at some time in the future when these massive, expensive machines (Stanford's 2-mile-long accelerator will cost $114-million) could be constructed of local materials. The cost also might be reduced somewhat on the moon since gettering ionization pumps normally placed every 20 feet could be eliminated and because the structure could be as flimsy as a spider web in the absence of wind and weight.

Acoustical electron phenomena was checked by 8.4% of survey respondents who saw advantages in studying the transmission of sound in an enclosed lunar volume. Such a space could start as vacuum and be changed, one step at a time, by the introduction of gases.

Strain on electrical conductivity was checked by another 8.4%. (But it is hard to find a reason why!) This and the more sensible *lattice specific heat* research, marked by 4.5%, complete the multiple-choice list of vacuum research reasons presented in the questionnaire.

In addition, 22% of the surveyed vacuumists suggested other areas of research that could be advanced significantly on the moon:

Energy conversion devices utilizing the unimpeded rays of the sun (effectiveness of any solar converter would be 62% greater than on earth); bearing and lubrication research in vacuum; the use of multiple-layer vacuum insulation for insulating experimental vessels as well as moon houses; all types of space simulation research, of course, including overall systems tests for spacecraft; development of ion propulsion engines; and even thermonuclear research in the absence of gas (which on earth provides a powerful cooling effect through a charge exchange of hot ions confined in a magnetic field).

Reasons for performing vacuum research on the moon seem as endless as the lunar void. It is the giant concept of attaining a wholly new environment of great area that is so intriguing — an environment that can be duplicated on earth only in tiny areas and at extreme costs and complexities, *"Now we don't need the Pump!"* is the reason for doing vacuum research on the moon and, when you say that, you immediately change the whole economics of vacuum technology.

It is as though we have lived these million years under the sea and have just now begun to exploit a new invention called the artificial nostril, which can be worn with some difficulty over our gills.

A scientist suggests that the oxygen in the thin gas above our homeland and over the land masses, and even the land itself, may have use in certain research and manufacturing processes, while at the same time allowing us to see the stars more clearly. (He says nothing of the excitement of exploration and hope for new knowledge undreamed, for fear he will disturb his less-imaginative colleagues.)

Massive 32-inch in diameter diffusion pumps — six of them —
must be used to bring pressure inside the 3,000-cubic-foot chamber at Fairchild's Space Environments Laboratory down to 4 x
10^{-9} torr. The unlimited environment available free on the moon
is a vacuum about 100,000 times better than that.

Explorers prepare to journey to the new environment, first simulating the conditions in small air chambers. But before they go, they need economic justification for the enormously expensive trip. Their governors are advised negatively by the court magicians, who "already know there is nothing of economic value" on the dry land, choked as it is by gaseous vapors.

Fortunately, the ruling party is up for election and wants to support new industries, particularly in the southern, northeastern, and far western provinces. The government also wants to get to the land before a certain rival nation does, and wants to show all the little nations that it has the power to do so first.

Thus, for the wrong reasons, the government supports the massive expenditures involved, and off we go to the "land of land" — to find a new dimension has been added to life and work. The air is useful after all; we now see the wisdom of building our steel mills and factories on land! ...

The analogy may be helpful if it dramatizes the utter folly of refusing to go to the moon, when the going is within our power, for practical reason upon practical reason, but always, essentially, for one reason: knowledge.

While it may appease the apathetic to say the surface of the moon will add to your knowledge, which is why you do research, the moon budget, as was the land budget in the parody, is in the hands of Congressional accountants and their cost-conscious Merlins.

The fact that research leads to profits should not have to be argued here. Suffice it to say that the approximately $225-billion being spent in the United States for scientific research in the decade of the sixties — about $56-billion of which is financed directly by industry without government funds — is not being expended without the profit motive. Certainly lunar research into vacuum technology will result in the production of new products and processes on earth.

More directly—perhaps by 1980, or only eight years after lunar research probably will begin—the knowledge and facilities so earned will lead to actual manufacturing on the moon.

Chapter **3**

WITNESS:

WHEREAS, the lunar research laboratory established to advance our knowledge of thin films, metals, coatings, components, superconductivity, cryobiology, and other physical properties and materials — as well as astronomy, geology, and exobiology — will provide a starting point for a production facility on the moon; and

WHEREAS, vacuum conditions exist naturally, and cryogenic conditions can be achieved simply through a device described herein; and

WHEREAS, the economical transportation of goods from moon to earth, and other apparent problems, will be shown to be solvable through innovation;

NOW, THEREFORE, the following arguments are presented to show why the moon is a desirable environment for manufacturing products both for use there and eventually for shipment to earth.

(TIME ESTIMATE for starting manufacturing operations on the moon: 1980.)

the case for manufacturing on the moon

THE REASONS FOR GOING to the moon seem no clearer to most men in this age than were the reasons for sailing westward in the time of Columbus. Both seem reversely mistaken in the context of their times, for the earlier exploration yielded considerably more than gold, and the present exploration will yield considerably more than prestige.

The wealth of the moon may not be so much a matter of finding rare metals (although this is certainly a possibility), but in taking advantage of the unique environment of boundless vacuum.

This chapter will attempt to show why the moon, some years hence, will be an ideal location for the economical production of certain types of materials, components, and systems. *The assumption must be made clear that manufacturing on the moon will be feasible only after a lunar research base has been established and only after transportation costs are re-*

duced, as will be estimated later. Yet, since we have paid part of the bill already, it is not too early to build lunar factories in our minds, the starting point of all accomplishment.

The survey of the American Vacuum Society membership, discussed earlier in its lunar research aspects, also sheds light on what products vacuum scientists and engineers consider to be eligible for moon *manufacture.*

Here are the answers given by the AVS respondents to the question "Which of the following devices or materials do you believe could be *produced* easier or better if the production were to be done in a moon factory?" Percentages refer to those vacuum specialists in favor of each type of production: vacuum cast alloys (70%), vacuum welds (56.8%), electron optical systems (28.4%), optical components (17.5%), pharmaceuticals and biologicals (13.3%), industrial chemicals (6.7%), petrochemicals (4.1%), plastics (3.3%), and "other" (5.8%). Among write-ins in the "other" category were vacuum-insulated tankage, energy conversion materials and devices, utilizing water-bearing rocks for liquid hydrogen and liquid oxygen rocket propellants, paper processing, and food processing.

The decision on whether a product could benefit from moon manufacture falls into two groups: moon-made items that can be produced *and used* on the moon (or in lunar-launched space), and moon-made items for earth consumption. The idea that markets one day may exist on planets other than the earth is not likely to infect many board rooms for the rest of this century.

At first thought, it would appear absurd to consider the moon as a site for smelting metals, casting alloys, welding, coating plastics, drying foods, or producing industrial chemicals or rocket propellants. The size and weight of the resulting products could not possibly qualify for shipment to earth. Yet, because of the advantages of production in large areas of vacuum and extreme cold, it is entirely practical to consider such products as eligible for lunar manufacture *if they are to be used,* as well as made, on the moon.

Where metallurgical research on the moon will concern itself primarily with purification studies, vacuum refining of metals and casting of alloys one day ought to be conducted on mass scale. Where inert gases are used on our planet to retard chemical reactions, lunarians will use vacuum. Where iron, nickel, and copper ores are refined on earth with reducing agents, they can be reduced easily by intensified solar heat alone on the torrid moon. Melting, welding, brazing, sintering, annealing, and single-crystal growth can be carried out full scale to build the pressure chambers, power stations, and land and sky craft for our future lunar base.

Most vacuum melting of metals and casting of alloys today are carried out in arc furnaces where high pumping capacity must be maintained to avoid parasitic arcs. These are arcs that sometimes occur between electrode and mold, and have been known to burn through to the water jacket and cause serious explosions.

Induction melting may be more practical for lunar use once nuclear or solar electricity becomes plentiful. The capacity of induction furnaces has risen sharply in recent years, to as high as 250 tons. The largest vacuum induction furnace today has a capacity of 15 tons, but its use on earth is limited severely because dozens of large oil diffusion pumps, blowers, and mechanical pumps are needed to evacuate the chambers to a level of only 10^{-3} torr. All this equipment could be eliminated on the moon where a much higher level of vacuum exists naturally.

A little-used and small-scale melting process — terrestrially carried on in either inert atmosphere or vacuum — may find growing use on the moon. It is levitation melting, a curious phenomenon in which a metal is melted while suspended, or levitated, in space without any contact with a crucible.

Metal powder or chips are placed inside a high-frequency coil and melted by induction, while the action of the electrical field on the metal causes it to float within the coil. Melting takes only a few seconds, is independent of any contaminating container, and results in a vigorous, thorough mixing of the melt. Again, vacuum is the reason for considering this on the moon, but the low lunar gravity also may prove advantageous for "lunar levitation."

On earth today, levitation melting is only a laboratory curiosity; conditions on the moon will not, by themselves, launch the technique into full-scale usage. The reason levitation melting is suggested here is to serve as one example of many techniques and processes that may get their first real start on the moon. For when men go to the moon, the same curiosity that brings them there will make them try various ideas that work imperfectly in the restricted vacuums of earth. The desire to experiment under new conditions is the stuff of creativity. It may turn out that the major usage of the moon is as a proving ground, a boundless, open-"air" pilot plant for vacuum and cryogenics processes to be employed elsewhere.

As Dr. Lloyd V. Berkner, president of the Graduate Research Center of the Southwest, Dallas, points out, "Manufacturing on the moon may not be established for at least the next several decades. But the lunar environment may offer the opportunity to develop experimentally certain manufacturing processes which, after being worked out, then can be established better on the earth."

While the smelting of lunar rocks, or the melting of metals, may be done by almost any terrestrial method, we may want to use plasma generators or electron beams because of their virtually unlimited temperature capabilities.

There is reason to believe that basalt exists on the moon in great quantities, as will be explored in the next chapter in the case for mining the moon. If so, a plasma torch could volatilize these rocks selectively, or fuse rock dusts. It should not be too difficult to supply inert gases from a tank to the plasma jet. The plasma flame vibrates with positively and negatively charged particles, but is surprisingly cohesive, stable, and electrically neutral. Plasma flames, at temperatures of 30,000 F or higher, can melt any known fusible material, and research is in progress now to determine the nature of fused rock particles when plasma flame spraying occurs in vacuum.

Electron beams may be especially suitable for melting and purifying refractory metals and semiconductors, both of which are sure to find their way into moon-made products such as rocket engines and electronic components.

H. A. Steinherz, in his valuable "Handbook of High Vacuum Engineering," states that to achieve electron-beam heating "it is generally desirable to use pure-metal cathodes such as tungsten or tantalum. This is unfortunate because other materials, such as oxides or thoriated tungsten, are much better electron emitters. However, they are so easily contaminated by exposure to the atmosphere, evaporated metals, or deposits of impurities that they are not very suitable for this work." The sterile, airless moon will favor their use, just as it will permit the use of naked metals which at home must be protected from contamination.

Electron beam welding on the moon could be scaled up for construction operations — especially for building spaceships. Because electron beam welding can do the almost impossible job of joining dissimilar refractory materials, such as metals to ceramics, it is supremely suitable for fabrication of ion propulsion systems.

Aside from the high heat potential, this type of welding eliminates contamination from an electrode, and it is possible to focus the diameter and power of an electron beam much more easily than an arc. Thus, smaller welds can be made. Electron beam welding probably would be more widespread on earth except for the very high vacuum requirement.

Tantalum, titanium, tungsten, molybdenum, zirconium, uranium, nickel, iron (in the form of stainless and carbon steels), aluminum, and beryllium have been welded successfully on earth with electron beams. As we shall see in the next chapter, these elements probably will be found near the surface of the moon. But if they prove difficult to mine, nickel and iron ores of amazingly high metallic content are lying around in ingot-sized hunks for our use in the form of unburned meteorites!

While electron beams probably will be used to weld metals of high melting point, those that melt at relatively low temperatures — aluminum, tin, and zinc — or at intermediate temperatures—copper, nickel, iron, and silver — may be welded on the moon simply by cleaning them with a wire brush, aligning, and holding their clean surfaces together. Starting with electronic components and lunar structures, applications on the moon for vacuum welding one day will be as innumerable as for nailing and gluing on earth.

Metals are not the only materials for lunar manufacture. The wonderful monotony of vacuum is one that begs for large sheets of something reflective: to construct microwave dish antennas for communications, solar reflectors, and enclosures for pressurized work areas or farms.

Unfortunately, the domed quarters that have become Sunday supplement synonyms for lunar living are not practical for space-suitless life — that is, unless they could be made of a puncture-proof material that

The lunar base should be located mostly underground for protection against micrometeoroids, as Republic Aviation Corp. drawing above indicates. Even the garden (in lower center of the picture) is underground, a precursor to pressurized and sunlit aboveground lunar farms of the future. Below, aluminum-coated "Mylar" — National Research Corp.'s "superinsulation" — is wrapped around a cryogenic dewar.

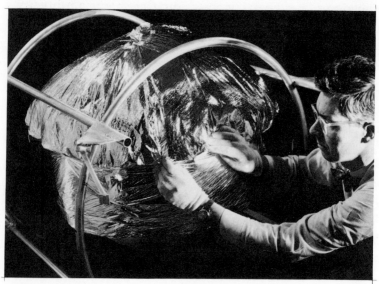

is a good heat conductor at one time, a good insulator at another, or both simultaneously. There is "rain" on the moon, the high-speed rain of micrometeoroids traveling as fast as 45 miles a second. The temperature and micrometeoroid problems are solved far more easily underground, and the pockmarked moon must contain thousands of lava tubes or mountain ledges hanging over crevices or craters for our prospective cave dwellers.

Rolls of flexible plastic sheet, such as Du Pont's "Mylar," fit the criteria of being lightweight for shipment from earth and easily supportable as non-pressure structures in the low gravity and stormless moon — provided they could be coated economically with aluminum or other reflectant metal. (One pound of aluminum is enough to coat 25,000 square feet!) Here the moon shines brightly, for its great expanse is a ready-made chamber for continuous coating in vacuum.

The only economical way to do vacuum coating of flexible sheets is in a continuous process. On earth, continuous coatings of plastic films using refractory metal filaments are hampered by heat transfer from source to substrate; the substrate sometimes heats at a rate that disrupts — and even chemically degrades — the plastic.

In attempts to solve this problem on earth, a molten pool of aluminum is used as the source instead of the tungsten filament normally employed in batch coating. In this way, unequal temperature distributions obtained when feeding wire against a refractory metal filament are avoided. But then other problems erupt due to the high solubility of most refractories: zirconia is insoluble in molten aluminum, but the lime that would be used for stabilization is reduced by aluminum; carbon forms aluminum carbide that goes into the melt and interferes with the evaporation ... and so on.

The moon environment will not solve the crucible

problem. It will sidestep it completely. For substrates on the moon will be thoroughly outgassed in perpetual vacuum long before we attempt to coat them, and tungsten filaments can be used, as in batch coating. Continuous vacuum coaters should welcome the milieu of our natural satellite.

They even may want to stretch miles of reflectant sheet over a large area of the surface, and use the resulting reflector as a communications satellite and relay station for television. (If you think this is far out, consider the Russian plan for plating the entire visible hemisphere of the moon, the natural albedo of which is very low, with a reflectant coating to make it a huge power plant in the earth sky!)

Eventually, we must face the problem of growing food on the moon. An enclosure only partly obscuring the effects of cloudless sunlight will be necessary, as will research toward optimum development of restless plants that will thrive in continual sunlight during the half-month growing season. Perhaps a combination of gibberellins (the remarkable family of jack-and-the-beanstalk plant regulators that has been used to produce 20-foot tomato vines); uninterrupted two-week periods of sunlight; and hybrid seeds developed for the purpose will revolutionize our ideas of the length of growing seasons.

If not, we need only to place our farms within translucent enclosures at one of the poles, where tangential sunlight steadily maintains 90 to 100 F temperatures, and no night falls for six months at a time. As for preserving the food we grow, research techniques such as dry freezing are applicable for scale up.

Micrometeoroid penetration would hamper operation of an enclosed, pressurized farm, but not to the extent that it would living quarters (which, unlike farms, can be built underground) since lunar farmers would not venture into the area without spacesuits.

This disadvantage may be compared to the myriad weather, insect, and other obstacles overcome by terrestrial farmers.

Now, obviously we will not land two or three men on the moon and expect them to build their shelters, grow their food, and start smelting iron. In the beginning everything will have to be imported at enormous cost, and the moon will crawl with "molabs," "lems," and "lunar hoppers" that will serve for housing as well as transportation. Thereafter, a more economical development of the moon as a base will necessitate greater and greater reliance on local materials.

Propellant production on the moon will be desirable when we can afford to get serious about saving money. A chemical plant established on the moon to derive liquid oxygen and liquid hydrogen — from underground water, ice, or minerals containing water as a constituent — would be a worthwhile investment at some point. Why not? The propellants could be sent from the moon to earth orbit, by a technique that will be described later, without using any rocket fuel at all and at a fraction of the cost of sending terrestrial propellants to the moon.

If ice or water cannot be mined in sufficient quantity, we merely need design a hydrogen-oxygen maker small enough to be boosted to the moon ready for operation, or simple enough to be constructed locally. Like the lunar still mentioned in Chapter II, the water maker must be mobile — not only to get to the choicest hydrous surface rocks, but, more important, to move readily from the intense heat of the day to the intense cold of the night. The relatively sharp demarcation between day and night has a speed of only ten miles an hour at the equator and, of course, much less at higher latitudes. It would not take much effort to cross that line, called the terminator, back and forth, at will.

Let us innovate. In operation, a shovel would pick

up some hydrous moon on the day side, crush it, and heat it with a solar furnace in an enclosure to evolve the water vapor. The hydrous moonrock would be heated to about 1200 F, the temperature at which dehydration proceeds rapidly.

The mobile water mill then would cross the terminator into night and condense the vapor by natural refrigeration. From there, it is only a matter of electrolysis to decompose the compound, and of submission once more to outside night temperatures (in the "lunar cryostat" to be described) for condensing at 20 K into liquid hydrogen and oxygen.

I do not mean to gloss over the technical difficulties of importing the components of such a mechanical shovel to the moon. But the first one, say in the late 1970s, could be fairly lightweight, large enough to convert moonstones into water for only a handful of personnel. As the lunar research base grows into a manufacturing site, appropriate-sized water mills and a wealth of other devices would be fabricated locally. Of course, the method of generating water suggested is considerably more complex than turning a faucet on earth, but there will come the day when such a scheme is less costly than the alternate solution of continuous supply from earth.

In the procedure proposed above, another natural resource of the moon has been utilized. It is the extremely slow rotation of the moon on its axis, which as we know just about equals the moon's revolution around the earth so that our little sister planet shows only her same hemisphere to us.

When I think about walking along the moon just ahead of the frontier between day and night, I can imagine whole bands of consistent temperature belts curving from pole to pole, moving slowly east to west in front or in back of the languid terminator.

This fact of lunar life can be exploited for manufacturing, just as can the other natural resources of vacuum, low gravity, moderately high heat, and fierce cold. For instance, a track extending along latitudinal lines could support a movable process the velocity of which could be timed to attain constant temperatures anywhere between −270 F to 260 F, or temperatures that decrease or increase at any desired rate.

Manufacturing on the moon surely will be different than on earth. It will not be inherently more expensive, though, after all trade-offs are balanced. Some things, like water, will cost considerably more than we're accustomed to paying; other things, like low temperatures and vacuum, are free. As in planning for any new industry or environment, the whole idea is to turn apparent liabilities, such as airlessness and long nights, into assets. Few problems cannot be solved by innovation.

So far, the intense cold of the moon at night has been discussed as an asset only for manufacturing processes requiring temperatures, available naturally, of about 105 K (−270 F). But as mentioned before, a simple "lunar cryostat"* could be assembled on the moon to reduce temperatures to 5 K or lower, thereby expanding our manufacturing horizons into processes that can benefit from large areas of inexpensively obtained temperatures in the superconductive range.

Although cold as low as 0.00001 K has been generated in conventional earth-based cryostats, the method is complex, expensive, and time-consuming, and the refrigerated volume is small. Many experiments and processes generate heat. It is one thing to cool a nuclear-spin system to a few microdegrees Kelvin and very much another to scale up such temperatures and heat-emitting objects for actual operation. Problems of thermal contact, thermal isolation, and relaxation times crop up in terrestrial cryogenics laboratories, and they are formidable.

*Patent pending by the author.

In order to arrive at a condition of essentially "no heat" on the moon, we must ask: what are the objects emanating heat and how can they be effectively blocked?

The prime source of heat energy, of course, is the sun. We can block that easily — for 350 hours* at a time at least — simply by conducting our cryogenic manufacturing processes during the 15-day-long lunar night, thus placing the entire mass of the moon itself between our cryostat and the sun.

A substantially lesser source of heat, but still an important one to eliminate, is the heat of the earth re-radiating the sun's energy across a mere 239,000 miles. Again we can utilize the mass of the moon as a shield, merely by locating the cryogenic site on the familiar "far side." The far side, or the side that never faces the earth, results from the fact that the revolution of the moon about the earth almost exactly equals its rotation on its axis.

Other heat sources in space — such as the few scattered hydrogen atoms in the vicinity of the moon and the distant stars — are negligible. A word about the energy flow (flux) of the stars:

The galaxy of which our solar family is a resident, 30,000 light years from the center, contains perhaps 100-billion stars. The greatest flux of radiation comes from directions lying close to the plane of the galaxy and from its center — it is the area we call the Milky Way. Calculations show that these and the other trillions of more distant stars in the sky would impart to a black body in solar system space — if there were no sun, earth, or moon — a temperature of only 3 to 4 K (a white, or reflectant body, would be even colder). Stellar distances count infinitely more than stellar quantities in this business of heat transfer.

*The number 350 is used approximately. The length of the day or night is exactly 354.1 hours at the lunar equator, but varies with latitude and season.

The only source of heat we need consider as we contemplate the star-speckled black of night is the mass of the moon re-radiating solar energy. It is necessary only to shield this heat effectively from the objects to be cooled. The lunar cryostat, then, consists simply of a series of dish-shaped insulator-reflector shields, stacked one on top of the other and held slightly apart by supports made of rigid foam plastic or other material of low thermal conductivity. The shields are dish-shaped to eliminate radiation from the moon's surface, including mountains:

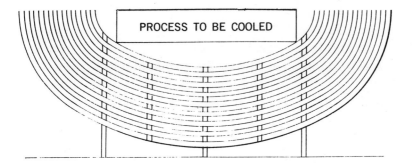

PROCESS TO BE COOLED

The insulator-reflector shields would be made of aluminum foil or similar material blackened on the upper side. Or, vacuum deposition of thin aluminum films on plastic sheets may be unusually suitable because manufacture of the lunar cryostat could be done in the vacuum of the moon and of moon materials. A superinsulation developed by NRC's Milo P. Hnilicka would be ideal for the job; it is metallized "Mylar," and requires no separators because the crinkling provides for sufficient separation.

The lunar cryostat will achieve ultra-low temperatures because each shield re-radiates heat from the original moon surface temperature at a progressively lower temperature until we reach the near-absolute zero temperature of sunless, moonless, earthless space.

The number of shields in the stack will depend upon the reflective and emissive characteristics of the material and resultant temperature desired. From 50 to 100 shields probably will suffice, but 1,000 or 100,000 could be confined to a few inches thickness utilizing metallized plastic films. Since the resultant temperature at the top of the stack of shields is a direct function of the number of shields, we might regulate the temperature by adding or subtracting shields. Removable groups of shields could be numbered near the edge with the temperature to be attained, such as 10 K, 9 K, 8 K, etc.

In the lunar vacuum there can be no heat transfer by convection. Heat transfer by conduction from the surface of the moon to the material of the shield is eliminated by providing a (vacuum) space between the shields.

Generation of heat within the component or process being cooled is the one remaining problem, and the only reason why temperatures below about 5 K cannot be attained by mere shielding. Achievement of lower temperatures, however, need only utilize adaptations of conventional cryostatic techniques, such as where copper wires leading from the process are cooled. Here, handling the liquid helium or other equipment on the moon would be immensely simplified in the hard vacuum, and with a temperature head start of some 300 degrees Kelvin.

As described, the weight of the lunar cryostat is minimal should we want to send some in assorted sizes to the moon. The one-sixth gravity and dead calm of a world where winds have not blown for billions of years require such a structure to be much less than a

A cryogenic factory on the moon might look something like this someday. The author's "lunar cryostats"—the dish-shaped structures shown outside the control room — will achieve temperatures near absolute zero economically and without size restrictions.

sixth as strong as its earth counterpart.

These lunar cryostats may be as small as a few inches in diameter, or as large as several thousand feet, depending upon their use. The distance between reflectors can be as little as desired for compactness, so long as they do not actually touch, since molecules will outgas rapidly in the lunar vacuum.

Considering outgassing — and purposeful degassing — the benevolent moon again lends a hand. During the long lunar day, the 260 F heat is useful for "baking" the cryostat and its subjects, ridding them of any remaining gas molecules. Such baking could be done at middle latitudes, if we like; the cryostat then could be moved poleward.

The alternation of day and night at the poles is slowed substantially, as on earth, and for the same reason. The inclination of the moon's axis gives us darkness there for six months at a time. It is as on our planet, except that the incredible, vacuum-deep blackness is as divorced from the nocturnal earth, whose air disperses starlight and moonlight, as our mile-deep seas are from daylight. Both have their "stars," incidentally: luminescent points of living light in the depths, and stellar furnaces in the heavens weakened by distances measured in light years.

And there are craters at the poles, particularly a large one at the south pole deep enough to prevent any sunlight, even during the six-month period of daylight, from ever reaching an object placed at the bottom. Because darkness equals cold on the airless moon, such an area might be the site for a cryogenics base should continuous usage of the cryostat beyond the normal night be desired, or should it be discovered that more than 350 hours of cooling are required to reach very low temperatures.

The lunar cryostat, though simple in concept, is significant, and thoroughly belongs to the moon. Cryogenic temperatures cannot be obtained as economically or easily anywhere else near earth. You can't achieve cryogenic temperatures easily in solar system space by shielding because of the tremendous energy of the sun. Nor can you get them with satellites when the earth occludes the sun. Satellite orbits are measured in minutes or a few hours, whereas it will take days to achieve cryogenic temperatures by radiation shielding from an already cold moon.

Even if you could find a way to utilize artificial satellites for cryogenics work, you would only be duplicating on a small scale our natural satellite, which has the decided advantages of size and of having been placed in orbit some time ago.

Given controllable, reproducible temperatures all the way up the scale from absolute zero, and given the natural vacuum of the moon, think of the ease of operating devices on the moon requiring this environment!

Consider superconducting magnets, virtually frictionless bearings for gyroscopes and motors, superconducting rectifiers, tunnel diodes, oscillators, and amplifiers, infrared detectors of unusual sensitivity, and superconducting transformers. All may be operated on the moon with appropriate-sized "lunar cryostats" beneath, eliminating the need for complex attendant refrigeration.

One of the most useful of cryogenic devices is the high-field electromagnet; we will need them on the moon for everything from moving masses of iron meteorites (and separating them from non-metallic dust) to research in thermonuclear fusion. Fine wires drawn from compounds or alloys with high transition temperatures, such as niobium-zirconium or niobium stannide, remain superconducting in high external electrical fields and also carry high current densities. Solenoids (kinds of electromagnets) yielding fields of more than

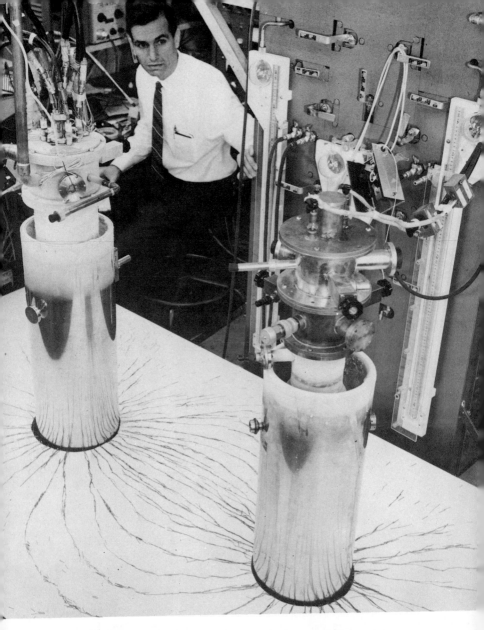

Iron filings on white table illustrate extremely high magnetic fields made possible by superconducting magnets at General Electric Research Laboratory. Stainless steel dewars and attendant refrigeration must be used to maintain liquid helium at 4.2 K. Simple heat shields on the moon would make possible cheap and widespread use of superconducting devices.

150 kilogauss* already have been made. Experiments indicate that such fields could be increased if cryogenic cooling could be extended.

Ordinary electromagnets can produce fields of this magnitude, of course, but not as easily. Superconducting electromagnets need no large heat exchanger; they occupy far less space; they develop stronger fields; and power requirements are relatively negligible — important considerations in the early stages of moon development. A lunar superconducting magnet, with no need to be immersed in a vessel of liquid helium as on earth, exemplifies the concept of utilizing unique local advantages in the conquest of new worlds.

Probably the greatest promise of superconductive materials is that they allow us for the first time to overcome the limitation of 20 kilogauss which has been imposed until now on the construction and design of electrical machinery and devices by the saturation of ferromagnetic materials.

With superconductive magnets, we can use fields up and beyond 100 kilogauss practically. (The GE device in the picture has achieved 132 kilogauss.) Equally important, such fields can be maintained, just as in permanent magnets, without any consumption of electrical energy — a fact of tremendous importance in the virgin lunar economy.

Nor are electronic devices the only beneficiaries of cheap cold. Cryogenic research (restricted unduly on earth) already has penetrated beyond the macroscopic superfluid systems occurring at low temperatures and into the realm of the atomic nucleus.

Absolute zero is defined as the hypothetical point at which all molecular motion ceases. But despite major gains in recent years, we are still whole orders of magnitude away from cessation of motion. As Dr. James

*A gauss is a unit used to measure magnetic induction, or intensity. One gauss is equal to one line of magnetic force per square centimeter. A kilogauss is 1,000 gauss.

Nicol and Dr. Conrad J. Rauch of Cryonetics Corp. pointed out in their article "Below 1 Degree K" (*Industrial Research,* September, 1964), the importance of temperature ratios tends to be overlooked. "If an object at 1 K is reduced by *only* 0.9 degree, its absolute temperature actually is reduced by a large factor of ten."

With the advantage furnished by the lunar cryostat, additional means may be found to achieve these factors, again and again, bringing us closer and closer to the cessation of motion and into the mysteries of matter and energy. We cannot go there yet, but we can go at least part way with our imaginations. Ultra-low temperatures might provide the key to gaining more precise control of chemical reactions. A controlled quantity of free radicals — atoms or ionized fragments of atoms that combine and release enormous amounts of energy — might be injected into a reaction at near-zero temperatures to effect major changes in polymers, monomers, organics — all chemicals.

Perhaps whole new orders of materials will be created, where instead of elements and compounds, solutions and dispersions, we will have as yet unnamed, undreamed combinations of energy-matter. If so, such a science may begin with true synthesis where we build with the original subatomic building blocks of nature.

The concept is discussed here instead of in the former chapter on research because production applications already have been devised. The harnessing of free hydrogen atoms trapped in cryogenic solids has been proposed as high-energy rocket fuel, which surely will be among the first products of lunar manufacture. According to National Bureau of Standards research, a propellant of 100% monatomic hydrogen would produce a specific impulse of 1,520 seconds, which is four times the thrust of conventional rocket fuels.

Breakthroughs like these and many, many more will

provide the economic stimulus for further development of the solar system and further expansion of science into other areas. If the space program has ultimate justification, it is this massive, cyclical stimulus of exploration begetting knowledge and knowledge begetting exploration . . .

All of the processes described above assume using lunar-manufactured materials or devices on the moon itself, or in space. But what of employing lunar factories developed initially for that purpose to make electronic components, thin films, electron tubes, optical components, pharmaceuticals and biologicals, and other small or unusual products, perhaps in the late 1980s, *for shipment to the markets of earth?*

The suggestion is reasonable if we keep in mind that the moon cannot be developed economically for one or a few scientific or industrial reasons, but that if it is developed for thousands of purposes, it will serve those thousands more economically, more easily, more creatively than conventional methods. Have we such shallow insight, so little experience with new industries on earth not to visualize the breakthroughs a whole new environment can create?

Basic to the feasibility of such unmuzzled thinking is a plan for sending to the moon some raw materials — whatever cannot be found or processed cheaper there — and returning the finished products to earth, all at low cost. Obviously a better method will have to be devised than building billion-dollar *Queen Mary*-sized craft to carry thousands of tons of fuel for trips both ways; few considerations kill an otherwise desirable plant location quicker than the lack of suitable transportation.

It is not for nothing that the great steel-making centers of the United States are poised on the shores of the Great Lakes downwater from iron ore deposits, nor will it be accidental that earth-moon and moon-earth transport will rely on natural planetary resources. What are they? Why, the vacuum and low gravity of the moon, and the atmosphere of the earth. The former presents superb conditions for launching, and the latter for braking.

A hundred years ago, Jules Verne shot his heroes to the moon with a space gun (neatly utilizing the services of ex-Civil War cannon designers). The shot from earth to moon was unworkable, except in fiction, for Verne's protagonists would have been squashed against the sides of their ship before it left the deep vertical tunnel he used as the cannon barrel. Ah, but trips moon-to-earth open the mind to literature rich in formerly unworkable ideas for catapults, space guns, and rocket sleds!

Long electromagnetic accelerators to serve as ground-based launching systems for spaceships were suggested by Dr. E. F. Northrup in "Zero to Eighty" in 1937. Other stories have suggested simple pulley-and-counterweight arrangements, mile-long pneumatic launch tubes, underwater launching utilizing a rocket's buoyancy, and long inclined tracks on which a sled-mounted spaceship comes racing down a mountain to be hurled up at the end like a ski jumper.

The latter system appears to be as popular as it is pointless. The movie version (certainly not the book as written) of Philip Wylie's and Edwin Balmer's "When Worlds Collide" used it. In 1964, a U.S. patent was granted for a launching method utilizing the idea. And the Russians reportedly relish the system for launching some of their satellites. The reason it won't work, of course, is that all of the energy gained coming down the slope is exactly lost on the way up. You not only would *not* gain added push, but would lose a certain amount of thrust due to friction.

Other independent launching schemes do make

sense, however. As long ago as 1950, Arthur C. Clarke was the first to suggest and work out details of a sled to launch spacecraft *from the moon* — without the use of rocket engines on the vehicles for thrust. Whereas on earth, the high gravitational forces and impeding atmosphere would mean the track would have to be 400 miles long to achieve escape velocity — even at 10 g (equivalent to the force of ten times gravity), and without solving the problem of burning up in the lower atmosphere — the story from moon to earth warrants a different plot. Clarke:

"Because of the almost perfect vacuum, the lunar escape speed of a mere 5,200 mph (as opposed to 25,000 mph to escape from earth) can be achieved at ground level without any danger from air resistance. And at an acceleration of ten gravities, the launching track need be only 19 miles long. [Or half as long at 20 g, etc.] It would be a massive piece of engineering, but a perfectly practical one, and it would wholly transform the economics of space flight.

"Vehicles could leave the moon *without burning any fuel at all;* all the work of take-off would be done by fixed power plants on the ground, which could be as large and massive as required. The only fuel that a space vehicle returning to earth need carry would be a very small amount for maneuvering and navigating. As a result, the size of vehicle needed for a mission from moon to earth would be reduced tenfold; a hundred-ton spaceship could do what had previously required a thousand-tonner."

At the end of the one-way trip, the moonship will find a heavy atmosphere, ready-made for fuelless braking.

In addition, earth-to-moon transportation will be enormously simplified once ground power-supplied catapults or launching tracks are installed on the moon. When not launching transports to earth, the launchers could be used to project reusable tanks of hydrogen or other moon-processed propellant to earth orbit for rendezvous refueling. Thus, a spaceship need leave the earth with only sufficient fuel and container weight to get it into orbit, a considerable reduction over currently planned vehicles that carry fuel for the whole trip *and* the return.

The location, the lack of restricting atmosphere, and the one-sixth gravity of the moon are so advantageous in this regard that if our planet like Venus or Mercury had no moon, we should consider putting one there!

The concept of reducing weight and fuel requirements by using stationary powered catapults, or other concepts achieving similar economy, are basic to any plan for lunar manufacturing. Assuming no nuclear engines or other major breakthroughs in rocketry (a dangerous assumption as has been proved so often on hindsight), what progress can we expect in cost reductions of chemical rocketships from earth to moon?

Dandridge M. Cole, consulting astronautical engineer for General Electric Co., has worked out detailed charts showing the expected drop in costs per pound, earth to moon. For the purpose of this discussion, only earth-to-moon transportation costs will be considered, since I prefer Clarke's method of fuelless transport back to earth.

Cole estimates that where the 1965 cost per pound is some $5,000, it will drop, as soon as 1980, to only $30 (see chart on next page). To do this, Cole assumes a two-stage parallel system with three tanks containing oxygen and hydrogen and three engines, capable of 8-million pounds of thrust.

The take-off mass of the rocket is 20-million pounds; payload is 1-million pounds. Throw-away hardware would weigh about 1.5-million pounds and could be produced for about that many dollars since all expensive hardware would be retained in the recoverable portion. Propellants for the orbit flight would cost about $2-million.

Thus, the direct operating costs for orbiting a pound of payload would be about $3.50. On this basis, lunar landing costs would not have to exceed $30 per pound. "This system does not include any radically new propulsion techniques and is presumably a conservative estimate of what could be done in the 1980 time period," says Cole.

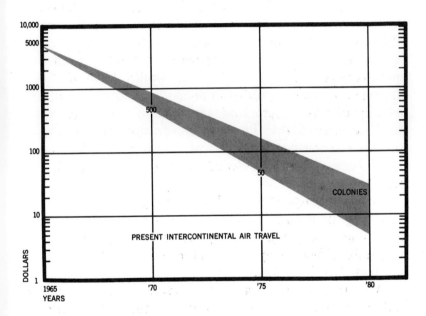

Combine these cost estimates with further reductions made possible by refueling in earth orbit with moon-processed fuel, and the cost of landing a pound on the moon in the 1980s easily could drop to $5, or about the same as present intercontinental air travel.

Energy requirements for space travel are not inherently greater, nor do they cost more, than for any other kind of travel. Today's high costs result from enormous development expenses on the emergence into a new technology and from the somewhat wasteful practice of throwing our spaceships away after using them once. The point is that transportation costs to the moon and back will come down when we establish a base and a technology there. How soon that happens and how far the costs will come down depends upon R&D budget decisions being made in Congress now and each year of this decade.

As for powering the launching sled to send payloads from moon to earth or projecting fuel to earth orbit, the power requirements seem ideal for a nuclear reactor. Solar energy converters in a cloudless sky appear sensible for power in the half-month day, but a solar converter on the moon, even operating at 62% greater effectiveness than on earth, still would have to be enormous to power multi-ton spaceships to the escape velocity of 5,200 mph. And what would we do during the long lunar night? Perhaps we can use solar energy for other lower-power electrical requirements for the moon base, or where electrical storage is less of a problem.

Nuclear reactors on earth are heavy, but primarily because of their massive shielding. The craters, crevices, and mountains on the unpopulated moon would provide natural shielding of a reactor assembled from one payload delivered from earth.

All other conditions — high power, long life, low fuel requirement, electrical output, ease of maintenance, vacuum for safe operation with no atmosphere to get poisoned — render a nuclear reactor a wise investment for the moon. Just as the underdeveloped nations of the earth have more nuclear power reactors than the technologically advanced nations, so the barren moon ought to enter industry using our most efficient power plants, and for the same reason: there is nothing there to start with.

Nuclear power plant designed to produce about 100 kilowatts of electrical power through a turbine-generator system is shown at extreme left in Westinghouse model of lunar exploration base. Continuing from left to right is a roving vehicle, excursion module, two six-man self-contained shelters, landing vehicle, another excursion module, and another landing vehicle. Albedo (reflectance of surface) of the moon is just about as dark as shown.

Westinghouse Electric Corp. recently designed a lunar nuclear power plant for NASA. The unit will produce about 100 kilowatts of electrical power through a turbine-generator system powered by the reactor. The entire plant could be contained within a single Saturn-V's 25,000-pound payload section — 20 feet in diameter at the base by 30 feet high. But it would appear that natural shielding, such as placing the reactor in a crater, could reduce the size and weight substantially.

As for the transmission of the reactor's electrical output, let's use wires!

Several scientists at well-known companies have suggested converting the power to microwave energy and beaming it with giant parabolic antennas to the mobile and stationary facilities and factories. Writers (including this one as early as 1950) proposed the future broadcasting of power to automobiles on earth to eliminate smog, gas stations, and other inefficiencies inherent in having 15-million terrestrial engines for 15-million vehicles. The economics of the idea may be noteworthy, but microwave beaming is not the breakthrough we've been waiting for; the beams spread exactly like a searchlight, diminishing with the square of the distance removed.

Given a source of electrical power and efficient transmission, economical transportation of goods to earth, and a lunar base, the next step — manufacturing at the colony to supply the mother country — is no more far-fetched than was the idea of exporting goods from Boston to London in the initial development of the American Colonies.

In considering candidates for our made-on-moon stamp, we have only to choose vacuum manufactured products that are small and lightweight, efficiently transportable to earth. Many electronic components fit this requisite, and production facilities already established to supply the lunar base will be in existence by

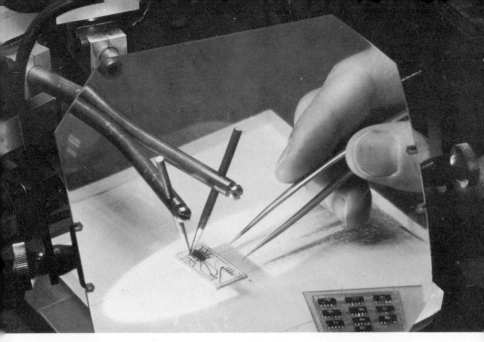

An electric circuit only a few thousandths of an inch thick is joined, above, to finer-than-hair wires with aid of magnifying glass at The Boeing Co. Vacuum-deposited circuits like this one, and the Bell Telephone Laboratories' integrated circuit, below, one day could be manufactured economically on the moon for shipment to earth markets.

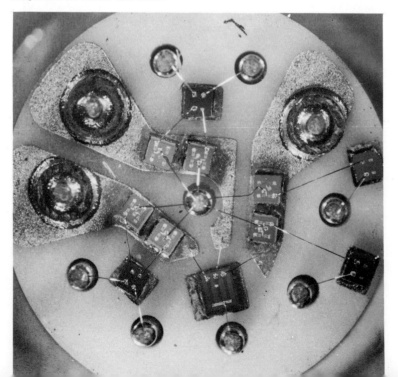

the time exportation is considered seriously.

Microelectronic circuits; computer components to remember, delay, switch, or amplify; unseen hearing aids; electric machines of many types; recording tapes; cathode-ray and other electron tubes; and guidance systems for space-cramped earth ships may be among the first moon products to reach earth markets.

Our "Continuous Lunar Coater" could prove invaluable for manufacturing capacitors and other components requiring coatings, as do microelectronic devices, or layers of resistors, or stacks of integrated circuits of semiconductor components such as field-effect transistors. The vacuum prevents oxidation of materials being coated and causes solvents or evolved gases to dissipate.

Vacuum tubes also are candidates for lunar manufacture. The benefits of unlimited vacuum and ease in sealing without leakage will take many years to override the advantages of continued expansion on earth and market proximity (as they will in all moon products). But the production of tubes requiring unusual configurations and very high vacuum, such as klystrons — where research and production are done simultaneously by moving the tube elements in vacuum for optimum performance — may find moon-making more economical than earth-making, despite transportation costs.

The moon never will compete with Japan for $5 portable radios or $12 microscopes, but it might well be a cheaper environment in which to manufacture 100,000-watt colossal light bulbs, which have been made recently on earth for photochemical processing applications.

Coating lenses and testing optical systems in vacuum also would be desirable, for air presents an ever-present interference mechanism on earth, and the systems usually are not too heavy to preclude long-distance shipment.

The great discoveries of this century in vitamins, hormones, antibiotics, tranquilizers, and other pharmaceuticals were made in sterile environments, and great purity continues necessary in processing. Since the raw materials of drugs are not particularly heavy commodities, but do require elaborate boiling, freezing, vacuum drying, and sterilization techniques, it eventually may prove *cheaper* to ship the raw materials to the moon for synthesis and then return the finished products.

If so, we even might take advantage of the ultra-sterilization of raw materials and supplies for the lunar drug laboratory during passage through the Van Allen and other radiation belts en route from earth!

Finally, one day, we may find it economical actually to send "some" of the moon's *vacuum* and lunar-cryostat-produced *cold* back to earth! The notion is not fantastic if you will but propel yourself some years into the future and observe the activity — the research stations, the factories and equipment, the hundreds of men — on the moon. Once this is reality, it is conceivable that a simple sealed pressure-shell containing literally nothing inside, or an insulated package of a material cooled to 10 K or lower, with suitable "vacuum locks," could be shipped to earth, ports intact — for a price less than evacuation or liquid helium cooling on mother earth.

Yet, no matter how far we reduce earth-to-moon transportation costs, bringing vacuum shells or raw materials *to the moon* for processing and return always will severely limit the manufacturing possibilities of luna. This may sound like a report to the Spanish Crown from the first governor of the Americas, but we must utilize local materials — not only for the making of products but also to reduce the great initial cost of sustaining life on the New World. Solving the problems of life support on an airless land and utilizing materials for manufacture depend upon what we find there —

and our ingenuity in transforming it.

Planetary engineers one day may alter the face of the moon. The selenologists, though, will swarm there first. When they do, it will be to answer important scientific questions about the origin of the earth and solar system, and to assess the mineral wealth of our second world. Only when knowledge (the simplest and most important commodity to ship) and locally manufactured materials are exported one way to earth will the moon begin to achieve its ultimate potential.

Chapter **4**

WITNESS:

WHEREAS, the earth has in orbit around it a sister planet about one-eighty-first its mass, probably consisting of the same materials as the earth, though in different proportions; and

WHEREAS, the moon has worked vigorously for some 4.5-billion years as a gigantic broom, sweeping up the iron and stone of solar system debris; and

WHEREAS, this ancient world has remained relatively unchanged since its formation, erosionless in the usual sense, without storms or winds;

NOW, THEREFORE, the following arguments are offered as to why the moon may be mined for materials of value and for knowledge of the origin of our earth, solar system, and stars elsewhere.

(TIME ESTIMATE to "mine" the moon for its knowledge: 1970; to mine the moon for its materials: 1985.)

the case for
mining the moon

THE MOON IS MADE of something. It came from somewhere.

Some few years after we set human foot on the moon, we can make more specific statements with the same authority expressed above, but now we know little else about the composition and origin of the moon with complete assurance. Yet it is difficult to imagine, whatever the moon is made of, that 81-quintillion tons of it will not be exceedingly worthwhile to possess. And however this little world came to be, that discovery most surely will add to our knowledge of the earth and the entire universe.

The case for mining the moon, then, is one case we shall win no matter what the outcome. Most of the raw materials of the earth are in increasing demand and many are in critically short supply. As for the mining of the moon's history, the more knowledge we extract from any source the larger becomes the source and the more fruitful our discoveries.

Having examined the practical utilization of the

moon's "atmosphere" in the last two chapters, let us consider what use can be made of the moon's surface and interior. If you listen to the critics, it is always too early to speculate. But speculation seems necessary to prediction, which is the major function of science. We must speculate if we are to predict the consequences of our contemplations; we must think if we are to do. Had Columbus speculated that the earth were big as well as round, he might have arrived on the new continent prepared to explore and develop it, instead of misnaming the thing and scurrying home.

Let us speculate.

Long before Galileo built his telescope, the ancients observed the one heavenly body on which they could see features, and thought they saw mighty seas surrounded by lands, an earth in reverse. These originally were called maria and terrae, and the words persist even now. Today we know the lands are higher than the seas and the light they reflect is redder than sunlight and somewhat redder than the seas. The seas have a lower albedo (reflectance) and relatively smooth surfaces between the craters all the way to their shores. Other than these differences, they are the same: both are considerably drier than any desert on earth; both are pockmarked with craters large and small; both, perhaps, are constituted partially of volcanic overflow underlying the ejecta of later meteoric bombardment; both are mostly covered with an inch or so of powdered moon.

You would get argument on the last two points, but less now than before the Ranger experiments. The Russian school long has held that the energy of micrometeoroid impact is sufficient to melt both the meteorite*

---

*The words "meteor," "meteoroid," and "meteorite" often are misused. Meteorists prefer the word meteor to designate a small body in space (or micrometeor if it's microscopic or macroscopic), meteoroid a meteor that has entered the atmosphere or gravitational pull of a planet or satellite, and meteorite a meteor that has fallen.

and the surrounding surface material, thus forming slag or rocky sponge. Even following the Rangers, fused slag proponents persist both in the USSR and here, claiming the shallowness of the covering layer means either that most micrometeoroids have hit with such force that they eject material from the impact point clear into space, or that the moon "dust" is fused.

The American school has believed that meteoric impact causes shock fragmentation but no appreciable fusion. Since the vast majority of impacting bodies over the billions of years were micrometeoroids, they would pulverize, forming a thin blanket of fine powder. To most selenographers, the Ranger pictures appear to confirm this, for if the material is fused, how did it subdue the crater rims? Those thousands of photographs are sharply in focus; yet the vast majority of crater edges are gently rounded. Neither a solar "wind" nor feeble gravity could soften the sharp edges of vacuum-fused slag.

This powder that covers most of the lunar seas and lands alike must be finer than the finest sand that sings aside the lakes of earth. Put your hand in some and let it trickle over your pressurized glove. It is fluidized flour without a fluid. It returns to the ground slowly, as in a dream or a colloidal dispersion. Like the sands of earth, the sands of the moon are silicates, but where the one is coarsely granulated, the other is powdered, and where earth sands fall when you drop them, moon sands seem to parachute softly downward, despite the vacuum, floating slowly in the extremely weak gravity.

Calling this substance "dust" may be a disservice to our sister moon; dust implies dirtiness and, according to Webster, "anything worthless." Some Pasadena physicists think it may have worth. They even now are studying the feasibility of using these free particles of the moon to replenish a spacecraft's power supply. The

Pasadena Research Division of Maremont Corp. is analyzing power-generation and propulsion through the use of charged particles, or colloids. Nuclear energy would be used to supply the electrical energy necessary for acceleration of a beam of tiny charged particles, thereby creating thrust.

These particles are not "fuel" in the usual sense—but they could be used as the mass expelled to provide a reaction thrust from the nuclear engines. Since the moon powder or other lunar materials must be similar to the colloidal particles employed in these studies, future spacecraft only need have tanks large enough to carry this mass on the trip to the moon. Once there, they could be re-"fueled" for the return or the voyage to planets elsewhere.

This use we can make of the moon's silent sand even without knowing its composition. But let's venture further.

There are reasons to believe that the "sands" of the moon are largely ferromagnesian silicates. First, the density of the moon is close to the uncompressed density of the earth's mantle, which is rich in this material. Second, the density is only slightly less than the average grain density of another similarly rich material, some of which must be pulverized among the lunar sands: stony meteorites, the most common variety of meteoritic matter.

This lunar "dust" will need no grinding. If it contains enough iron, it could be processed through the usual methods of magnetic separation. If not, it could be leached with acids and selectively precipitated until it contains only sodium and potassium salts, which then can be concentrated and electrolyzed to yield these metals or their hydroxides.

G. E. V. Awdry, writing in the *Journal of the British Interplanetary Society* in May, 1954, said, "Whatever else is scarce on the moon, oxygen will be abundant. A ton will be extracted in the reduction of 2.6 tons of iron, or 1.1 tons of aluminum, 1,000 days' supply for a man, with no recycling." He suggests the oxygen, after liquefaction, will be useful for blasting. Since the tools of the lunar prospectors must at first be simple, boring may be done with nothing more than a sledge hammer and an iron pipe burning in oxygen fed through it. Such a method, already in use, will melt concrete.

It is reasonable to suppose that the surface of a world the size of the moon varies substantially from place to place. Sulfur, almost always found in fractures near volcanoes on earth, well may occur in free form or sulfides in the hardened lava of the moon.

Brush aside the sands covering a volcano or cone where ancient gases once found outlet. Collect the underlying sulfur flow and deposit it into a small nearby crater, the bottom of which could be covered by a large sheet of metallic-coated plastic to prevent assimilation into the stuff of the moon. The crater now becomes a crucible during the long lunar day, since sulfur melts easily at 235 F and the sunlit surface of the moon rises to 260 F for almost 15 days at a time.

Where you find volcanic sulfur, you usually find lava caves and tubes. Once melted, this pale yellow mortar could be used to seal the cracks and fissures of drained lava pockets for shelters. Lava tubes seem to be the most promising areas of housing for initial moon bases because, already there, they provide protection from heat, cold, and cosmic radiation, as well as from the rain of micrometeoroids.

Dr. Jack Green and North American Aviation Inc.'s Geosciences Laboratory, which he directs, probably have done the most work to date on analyzing the "geology" of the moon for practical purposes. Green suggests that lunar sulfur can be used not only as a waterless cement and sealant, as described, but also to make bricks when mixed with volcanic ash or spun basalt fibers.

He envisions a primitive sulfur technology on the moon starting with sulfuric acid, possibly manufactured with the use of anaerobic Thiobacilli. These are bacteria active in the absence of free oxygen, deriving their energy from oxidation of sulfides, sulfates, or elemental sulfur. Once we have sulfuric acid, we can manufacture fertilizers for the hydroponic farms, make explosives to blast out our factory sites, and manufacture other chemicals necessary to sustain a manned lunar base and, ultimately, an industrial city.

With sulfuric acid and sulfur in other forms we can reduce certain metals, inhibit polymerization, polish surfaces and mirrors, lubricate pumps and other machines, separate minerals using low-temperature sulfur as a low-viscosity working fluid, transport rock fragments to the water extraction chamber using high-temperature sulfur as a high-viscosity fluid, and, finally, utilize this versatile hot liquid as the working fluid in power plants or the moderator in nuclear reactors.

Green suggests storing and transporting sulfur in cast basalt pipes. These are more corrosion-resistant to sulfur than metal pipes, and basalt is certain to be plentiful on the moon—not only because some of the craters may have been formed by volcanoes, but also because other evidence indicates the maria are of igneous origin.

If volcanoes existed on the moon, we are in luck in another way too. Volcanic rocks on the average contain ten times more water than most other basic rocks or meteorites. Although the variation is great, volcanic rocks hold an average of about 1% water, as opposed to a tenth this quantity for the average of meteoritic rocks.

The mining and manufacture of water doubtless will be one of the most important activities on the moon—for drinking purposes and, after decomposition into hydrogen and oxygen, for rocket propellants and oxygen to breathe. Unusual machines, like the mobile water mill described in the last chapter, conceivably could cross the slowly moving terminator from the bitter cold of darkness to the torrid day, back and forth at will, crushing, heating, condensing, decomposing, liquefying, extracting the simplest of elements from what might be the rarest of lunar compounds: water.

Even if water is not combined in lunar rocks — a possible though fantastic improbability — a chemical process now has been developed to produce both water and oxygen from silicates and other non-hydrous rocks. The process resulted from a NASA-funded research project at Aerojet-General's Chemical Products Division in Azusa, Cal.

First, a small nuclear reactor-powered furnace uses methane gas to convert lunar rock to carbon monoxide and hydrogen. Next, the carbon monoxide and hydrogen, pumped to a chemical reactor, are converted into methane and water. In the final step, water is broken down by electrolysis into hydrogen and oxygen. The oxygen would be stored for use by the lunarians; the methane and hydrogen would be recycled through the system.

The point I would like to emphasize is that scientific ingenuity already has devised methods of life support for the moon that are independent of earth supply and are, therefore, potentially economical. This carbothermal chemical process or an adaptation of it would be operative for *any* hypothesized composition of lunar minerals and is *completely independent of the presence or absence of water in lunar rock.* In other words, *whatever* the moon is made of, we can use it to make water and oxygen!

Most likely, we won't have to go to that much trouble, however. Water probably is combined in volcanic extrusives or volcanic sublimates as well as in nonvolcanic hydrous rocks and meteorites. Or we may be fortunate and find permafrost or ice in permanently sealed pockets of volcanic craters.

Green compares a part of the moon with the Arco Tunnel at the Craters of the Moon National Monument, Idaho, a fitting analogy. Here, ice stalactites formed in caves many decades ago continue to grow, a drop at a time, insulated from the earth's ambient temperature. The origin of these icicles is surface run-off water. Whether a somewhat similar process could take place on the moon, no one knows, but the possibility certainly exists.

Among those who disagree is Ralph B. Baldwin, author of "The Measure of the Moon" and other lunar books; he is vice president of Oliver Machinery Co., Grand Rapids, Mich. Baldwin believes that many gases, liquid water, and various hydrocarbons would have been extruded upward in a melting moon and have reached the surface some billions of years ago. If so, they will have been lost because of the moon's low gravity. He argues for a hot interior of the moon, though not so hot as in earlier times. "Being hot, the moon should occasionally emit gases as a remnant of an earlier heat cycle or as a forerunner of a new cycle. Being hot and solid, with buried radioactivity, it is possible that the moon is preparing to undergo another, or third, heat cycle."

Reasoning from such assumptions, some speculators have postulated that water vapor evolves even now from the interior and remains as ice in permanently shadowed zones. But the vacuum of the moon is much harder than 10^{-11} torr—the vapor pressure of ice in the cold shadows of the moon — and so ice would sublimate rapidly and its water vapor dissipate unless completely trapped in some tightly sealed "sub-selenian" pocket.

Icicles in a tunnel at the Craters of the Moon National Monument, Idaho (of all places), could have their counterparts in lunar caves, according to some selenographers. Source of the water would be internal instead of from the surface as in the picture.

It is difficult to predict the presence of free water, let alone its quantity. Hydrous rock appears a safer source for planning our water supply. Volcanoes on the moon, whether extinct or active, would provide good grist for our water mill: an average 1% (by weight) water-bearing volcanic rock would yield between one and two quarts per cubic foot.

Yet our desire for a volcanic moon hardly testifies to its existence, any more than the ancient longing for a habitable moon of maria has poured water in the lunar lowlands. An astronomer looking at the moon will tell you that all the craters probably were formed by the impact or explosion of countless meteoroids. A geologist, theorizing from inexact measurements of great earth-produced land tides, from the low lunar gravity, and from his knowledge of terrestrial volcanism, will tell you that most of the craters probably are volcanic. Indeed, these biases were reflected by the survey of 1,000 astronomers as compared to another of 1,000 geologists. The question, asked of both groups: "Do you think the impact (meteoritic) theory or the volcanic theory best explains the cause of lunar craters?" elicited these responses:

GEOLOGISTS		ASTRONOMERS
8.3%	Meteoritic	22.1%
8.4	Volcanic	4.3
30.2	Both, but mostly meteoritic	46.7
42.0	Both, but mostly volcanic	16.9
11.1	No opinion	10.0

Baldwin, on reviewing this manuscript, suggested, "You have used the proper word—'biases.' Out of 1,000 astronomers, there are probably not more than 50 qualified to answer your question concerning the nature of the lunar craters and an even smaller number in the 1,000 geologists."

Certainly the truth of scientific theories cannot be

determined by popular vote of scientists. The information above, indicating the current state of belief among geologists and astronomers in the United States, is presented to suggest that the 90% who have definite opinions would do well to keep an open mind. The same is true for the experts, for even they are far from agreement as to the origin of the craters. (Because there is such diversity of opinion, it is unfortunate that only about 2% of NASA funds earmarked for lunar crater simulation and research are directed toward volcanology. This percentage of funded effort contrasts with about 50% for impact hypotheses and 48% directed for crater research of no specific hypothesis.)

As with almost all other questions about the moon, arguments can be found to lend credence to almost any theory. One, bearing on the problem of volcanism and water potential, is especially lively. Only a few years ago, several somewhat reactionary scientists concluded that if the moon had been born hot and cooled early, deep seas and an atmosphere of water vapor would have formed. The atmosphere, replenished continuously from the seas, would last for 3-billion years, they calculated, making free lunar water extinct for only the past 1.5-billion years or so.

Apparently they hadn't read, or believed, the famous astronomer W. H. Pickering (no relation to the W. H. Pickering who is director of the Jet Propulsion Laboratory). Astronomer Pickering, in 1903, crippled the idea of free water bodies ever having existed on the moon when he wrote:

"The lunar atmosphere, on account of the gravitative constant, can never have been very dense, like our own, and the rapid evaporation from extensive lunar oceans under low pressure and exposed to the tropical rays of the sun would have produced deeply eroded valleys and extensive river systems, which are conspicuous on the moon only by their absence."

On earth we feel the force of the moon, and to a lesser extent the distant sun, in ocean tides that surge as high as 50 feet up cliffs of certain bays. It is so on the dry, but flexible and smaller, moon where *the land* at perigee* bulges as much as 13.5 times greater than it does on earth, and at apogee 9.1 times greater. Two components of the same earth-force are present here. The earth pulls the surface of this little world 81 times harder than the moon pulls the earth. And the pull is irregular: greater at perigee, weaker at apogee, but considerably more complex than that. The sun adds its influence to the earth's twice each month, when the earth is full and again when it is a dim thread of silver in the lunar sky. When the earth is either full or new and simultaneously in perigee, the land tides are unusually severe. At quarter phases of the earth, the terrestrial pull is partially neutralized by the sun and the tides are weaker at perigee and weaker still at apogee. Long ago, when the moon was young, and perhaps even now, these powerful and constantly varying attractions of earth and sun could have created fractures, triggering eruptions and even volcanism.

How about direct observations of volcanic action on the moon? After all, if volcanoes once existed, a few still might be active. And if active volcanoes exist, why can't we see them?

A few years ago, some scientists may have done just that. A Russian astronomer, N. A. Kozyrev of the Crimean Astrophysical Observatory, on Nov. 3, 1958, was making a spectrogram of the crater Alphonsus, near the middle of the lunar disc as viewed from earth, when he saw the central peak become strongly washed out and turn slightly red. He observed it visually, took a spectrogram then, and made another two hours later

Perigee is the point in the orbit of the moon when it is closest to the earth; apogee is when it is the farthest.

when the brightness of the peak suddenly fell back to its normal value. The latter photograph showed a series of bright emission bands superimposed on the usual spectrum. Kozyrev interpreted the event in this way: first, volcanic ash was ejected, accounting for the red appearance in the eyepiece of the instrument; then gases emanated from the peak producing the emission spectrum of the carbon molecule C_2.

Few professional astronomers spend much time observing the moon, and the fact that Kozyrev happened to be aiming a spectrograph at that particular crater on the moon at that particular time was a rare event. Increasing the coincidence, two physicists of General Dynamics' Convair Division in San Diego, both amateur astronomers, just happened to be looking at that part of the moon with a reflector of 6-inch diameter, at precisely the same time. They were startled to see a diffuse cloud they estimated at 20 miles in diameter completely obscure both Alphonsus' central peak and its small adjoining crater. In addition, every few years during the last hundred or so, others have reported some sort of gaseous eruption on the supposedly dead moon.

In the tight circle of science, an experiment or observation is not accepted as fact, fortunately, until it has been corroborated — repeated with like results — by other scientists. Unfortunately, these lunar incidents were not corroborated. In fact, another amateur astronomer claimed he was observing Alphonsus at the same time and saw nothing.

Then, six years after Kozyrev's observation, a new NASA instrument called a "moon blink" was pressed into service to search the lunar landscape for anything unusual. The instrument locates spots of color on the moon by making them appear to blink; the blinking effect is produced by color filters rotated across the light reflected by a telescope mirror.

The red spot near the center of Alphonsus blinked prominently through the instrument, right where Kozyrev spectrographed it! His event was verified — if not his volcanic deductions therefrom.

Afterwards, some scientists suggested other explanations for Kozyrev's and NASA's photographic evidence. For instance, Dr. Harold C. Urey of the University of California, San Diego, said: "It is difficult to understand how C_2 could be produced this way ... No gas containing two atoms of carbon has ever been reported from terrestrial volcanic sources."

Urey believed that the famous geologist G. K. Gilbert proved conclusively, 70 years ago, that the features of the moon are not due to volcanoes. That was before Ranger IX landed in Alphonsus on March 24, 1965. Later, Urey and other scientists who had so ridiculed the idea of lunar volcanism began to change their minds (as any good scientist is perpetually prepared to do).

Even Ranger IX could not prove volcanism beyond any doubt, but the evidence is so strong now that most scientists today admit the existence of at least some volcanism. Whether there has been enough to result in widespread volcanic materials is now the big question, which probably will have to await answer until men land on the moon.

Against this bewildering background of conflicting theory, are there any highly valuable materials to be found on the moon? Diamonds are known to exist in trace quantities in some meteorites; since meteorites are plentiful on the moon, it is conceivable that we might extract diamonds for profit in some advanced lunar technology. Platinum has been found both in meteorites and in volcanic rock on earth.

If we can find platinum on the moon—which in addition to being an expensive, precious metal is in such short supply on earth that substitute materials already are sought to replace its use in fuel cells and catalysts—we most certainly will want to ship most of it to earth. The Associated Press recently quoted "some experts of NASA" as saying that there "are" platinum metals in the 3-mile diameter asteroid Ivar, $50-trillion worth—or enough to finance one hell of a space program, eliminate poverty, retire the national debt, educate the people of earth, and maybe even dig the Mohole! And if you say price would drop as rarity vanishes, asteroid miners could counter by snaring a few more tiny planets consisting of still other priceless materials.

General Electric's Dandridge M. Cole has worked out detailed plans for capturing asteroids, utilizing the low gravity and lack of atmosphere of the moon for economical launchings of spacecraft. He wants to do this as early as the middle 1970s, envisions asteroids as filling stations for chemical rocket propellants, and suggests hollowing out these big planetary rocks as a further step in the colonization of the solar system.

Trace quantities of platinum, other noble metals, and diamonds exist in the asteroids because they exist in meteorites, most if not all of which were asteroids at one time. Thus the noble metals are present on the surface of the moon, the vacuum-preserved graveyard of meteorites in our part of space.

Nor is meteorite collection our only hope for finding precious metals. Platinum, silver, copper, and mercury undoubtedly exist on the native moon in at least trace amounts if the moon is partly volcanic. The platinum metals—platinum, palladium, rhodium, ruthenium, iridium, and osmium—are found on earth in basic igneous rocks; they occur in impure ores commonly mixed with iron. Silver is found in ore veins near volcanoes, combined with calcite and silver sulfides. Copper too is found in volcanic rock and ancient lava flows, often alloyed with small amounts of silver, arsenic, and iron. Mercury comes out of volcanic regions

Asteroid capture with strapped-on rocket tubes might look something like this in a day when lunar-launched workships are economical. Below, a NASA Surveyor spacecraft is fitted with instrumentation. Surveyors test the hardness and/or depth of "dust" of the moon's surface prior to manned landing.

both elemental and combined with the red sulfide of mercury called cinnabar. Because it solidifies at −40 F, mercury always is found in liquid form on earth, but may be discovered in solid state on the cold or shaded moon.

Smaller worlds, and worlds of lower mass, generally cool more rapidly than larger ones, and so should have thicker crusts, less stratification within the crust, and fewer concentrations of dense materials at their centers. Consequently, the moon ought to have crusts that are relatively richer in the heavy metals described, as well as in tungsten, tantalum, and uranium.

These precious and earth-rare metals are the materials we would ship earthward if they exist in sufficient quantities and purities close enough to the surface to be mined easily. Sulfur, basalt, water, and lunar sand would be kept on the moon for use there.

Speculations about the materials we may find on the moon conjure ideas of a less speculative comparison: mining our oceans and sea bottoms right here on earth. Trillions of tons of nickel, molybdenum, zinc, zirconium, and other valuable minerals are locked in our own ocean plants, rocks, and sediments. Incredibly large quantities of black, potato-shaped nodules are known to exist on the bottoms of deep oceans, containing 25% manganese and as much as 1% cobalt, copper, or nickel, and the deposits are forming faster than world consumption! Meanwhile, natural gas pockets recently have been found under the North Sea, and diamond placer deposits off the southwest coast of Africa (though mined so far only superficially) are yielding five carats per ton—a diamond ore five times richer than normal.

The point that must be emphasized concerning moon mining is not that we should go to the moon in order to find iron or platinum, but that once there it would be foolhardy to rely solely upon supplies from earth for any appreciable length of time. Such dependence upon earth would make development of the moon an impossibly expensive proposition. On the other hand, if we develop the moon with long-term goals in mind, we still may reap the benefits of a diamond or platinum rush as an important byproduct of the space effort.

What other materials may we expect to find on the moon?

Advancing the volcanic theory a step further, it appears likely that all of the elements and compounds concentrated in sea water on earth—except those of low vapor pressure that will have evaporated in the lunar vacuum—might be found on the moon in unknown quantities. Several Soviet geologists have suggested that undersea volcanism on earth has enriched the sea water in certain compounds, as well as supplying part or most of earth's water. Oceans did not form on the moon, so evaporites could not have been deposited. But even as the water escaped, other compounds supplied from igneous rocks and enriched in volcanic vapors may have remained near the surface.

In order of their likely quantities, the elements represented in these compounds would include sulfur, chlorine, fluorine, zinc, lead, boron, arsenic, bromine, iodine, antimony, cadmium, mercury, and selenium.

Numerous observations have been made of moon surface materials by reflected light and by heat measures. Some investigators feel that the former supports lunar volcanism, for most of the moon is dark gray, and although many materials reflect light identically, they find it hard not to envision stony meteorites in the lighter regions; volcanic ash, pumice, and slag in the places of medium reflectivity; and basalt, black lava, and obsidian in those with the lowest albedos. Radio and radar beams, on the other hand, consistently indicate the covering material is loose powder, a probability apparently corroborated by the Ranger VII, VIII, and IX pictures. But what lies beneath the lunar "dust" is as much a mystery as before the recent successful Ranger shots.

Before leaving the potentialities of volcanism, I would like to describe a fantastic though perfectly possible—no, probable—feat of engineering: the generation of great quantities of electricity, chemicals, and metals on the moon from geothermal (or selenothermal) steam.

California companies with the descriptive names of Magma Power Co. and Thermal Power Co. have been routinely producing 250,000 pounds of steam an hour to operate a 12,500-kilowatt plant that serves a community of 50,000. All over the earth today plans are taking shape to exploit the free heat from magma that has worked its way upward to within only a mile or so beneath the surface. If by the year 2000 half of all electric power in the U.S. will be nuclear, as has been estimated recently, a significant portion of the remainder may be geothermal, and both these sources doubtless will be even more important in the developing nations which have neither precedent nor fossil fuel.

While there are no lunar volcanoes rivaling Fujiyama, hundreds of crater domes resembling terrestrial shield volcanoes or laccoliths dot the lava-colored areas of the moon. These broad domes with gentle slopes, reminiscent of the active volcano Mauna Loa and the extinct Mauna Kea on Hawaii, probably possessed highly fluid lavas that have spread out for many miles in thin sheets. Most laccoliths are found in the not-so-appropriately named Mare Tranquillitatis, as well as in Mare Nubium, and especially Oceanus Procellarum.

Come along to the arid basin of the great greenish-gray ocean Procellarum. It is near the western limb and just above the equator. Here a peculiar plateau,

Rümker, leaps suddenly out of the deep sea to a height of half a mile, fanning into a rough circle 30 miles in diameter. As we approach closer we see hundreds of hills, or domes, each an igneous intrusion, perhaps an extinct volcano. At one of the larger ones men are working cumbersomely in diving-like suits, as though Procellarum truly were an ocean. They are drilling into the magma a mile, two miles deep. Their molybdenum drill bit, heated to 3000 F, eats into moonrock like a hot pick into ice.

Then it happens.

Hot volcanic gases explode into the vacuum, silently but visibly, a thousand feet high before dissipating into space. Quickly the workers cap the well, routing this superheated, supersaturated gas through a separator to remove the rich mineral brine and valuable water. This is "active ore," a fluid of boric acid, carbon dioxide, ammonium bicarbonate, steam, and metals in solution. The hot gases that are left, only slightly cooler for their ordeal, are harnessed to a turbine-generator unit that will provide electrical power in megawatts to the lunar colony.

Visionary? Not if volcanism exists on the moon.

Astronomers (and many geologists) prefer the meteoroid formation of practically all, if not all, lunar craters. If there were no volcanoes on the moon, sulfur would not be plentiful; platinum possibly as rare as on earth; copper, silver, and mercury in short supply; and the halogens, zinc, lead, boron, and other sedimentary-type elements probably nonexistent. But any world must be heterogeneous. Probably some, if not most, of the lunar craters are meteoritic, and the domes and craters within the dark, apparent lava flows are volcanic or at least of igneous origin.

Whatever the cause of the craters, however, iron and nickel do exist there in great quantities. To a lesser extent we are sure to find cobalt, chromium

Lengths of pipe aboard the vessel "Cuss I" are driven into the ocean bottom in first phase of Project Mohole. Molybdenum drill bits heated to 2190 F are proposed for actual three-mile hole into the Mohorovicic discontinuity — about the same time man will land on the moon. The technique of heating a refractory metal bit to melt rock might be used on the moon to drill for steam, water, and valuable minerals. Molybdenum melts at 4740 F.

(which can be vacuum rolled on the moon to make it more malleable), copper, phosphorus, carbon, aluminum, magnesium, sodium, potassium, calcium, and titanium. Why so certain? Because even if these elements are not locked in native ores or compounds as on earth, they definitely repose on the surface of the moon as the great and small chunks of the universe we know as meteorites.

The first iron industry on earth used meteoritic iron. The first industry on the moon will do so too.

Not only iron, but also meteoritic *steel,* was used by prehistoric man and by the Eskimos as late as the last century. The "Caille iron" in the Paris Natural History Museum, for instance, is a hard and rigid steel meteorite with high nickel and low carbon content. It is a fragment of a single meteorite of tonnage size. Since such large ingots of cosmic steel have been found and used *on the earth,* thus having survived fiery plunges through our oxygen-rich atmosphere, the airless moon ought to contain iron and steel on its surface in plenty.

The earth and moon travel closely together through the universe. But whereas the first hostilely incinerates the greater part of its cosmic visitors, the moon welcomes them, digging a monument appropriate in size to the importance of each. Actually, these crater monuments are considerably larger than the meteoroids that made them, so that it is easy to be misled as to the size and number of the fallen bodies.

Even so, it has been calculated that more than 70-million meteors bright enough to be seen by the naked eye enter the earth's atmosphere *every day!* The deposit on an earth without atmosphere would be of the order of 100 tons of meteoritic material daily. (One hundred tons is the conservative estimate. Others range upward to as much as 20,000 tons per day.)

Extrapolating the 100-ton figure to the smaller

moon, eight tons would fall each day. Actual tonnage would be somewhat less than that because the moon's planetary attraction is less, but not proportionately so since the gravities of earth and moon combine to alter meteor orbits.

If only six tons fall each day, 2,190 tons would fall a year, and about 9.9-trillion tons will have fallen in the 4.5-billion years since the moon was formed. While a little of this material might be deflected back to space along with some of the meteoroid ejecta, almost all of it shatters, pulverizes, explodes, or stays intact. One way or the other, *it remains on the moon.* Therefore, let us assume that 9-trillion tons of meteoritic matter exist on or within a few feet of the surface or are mixed into the surface powder.

Almost 93% of meteorites in the earth-moon region of space are stones, and most of these are chondrites, which are structures containing chondrules, or spheroids of silicates and other minerals less than three millimeters in diameter. Since chondrules are not found in terrestrial rocks, they are our clues that a rock is a meteorite. Of the chondrites, those of the most importance as raw materials are carbonaceous chondrites because they contain *as much as 10% water* as well as usable amounts of elemental sulfur, ferrous oxide, and various compounds of carbon.

Carbonaceous chondrites constitute 3.3% of all meteorites examined on earth, and so there should be 300-billion tons of them on the surface of the moon, or enough to provide 30-billion tons of water from this one source alone—that is, if they all didn't lose their water by vaporization on impact.

If, as Harold Urey once suggested, chondrites discovered on earth are not meteorites in the usual sense, but are fragments of the moon's surface—and if the carbonaceous variety constitutes its usual proportion of chondrites—the maria may as well be seas, for we shall not thirst on the moon.

Lunar ore probably can be found rich enough to warrant beneficiation, and volcanic basalt may be melted for castings as is done in Czechoslovakia and Poland. But both would have to be quarried. Convenient ingot-sized hunks of almost pure iron-nickel meteorites, meanwhile, merely need be gathered (perhaps magnetically) and melted, rolled, or otherwise formed.

About 5.7% of meteorites are the iron-nickel type, averaging about 88% iron, 6% nickel, 1.9% phosphorus, 1.8% carbon, 1.2% copper, 0.6% cobalt, and lesser amounts of other elements. Applying the same calculations, there must be at least 449-billion tons of iron, 31-billion tons of nickel, 9.7-billion tons of phosphorus, 9.2-billion tons of carbon, 6.1-billion tons of copper, and 3-billion tons of cobalt in still-existing meteoritic surface material on the moon. The third classification of meteorites, stony irons, constituting 1.5% of all cosmic visitors, would increase these composite percentages even more, to say nothing of similar metals occurring naturally in the moon's crust.

I am sure meteorists will argue with these generalizations, righteously and sensibly pointing out that we do not know whether the meteorite falls observed now can be averaged throughout the history of the earth and moon, or whether such falls have been sporadic occurrences; that perhaps almost all meteoroids have been vaporized in explosion or returned to space and thus never became meteorites; that many if not most may have been pulverized beyond recognition; and any that may exist as ingots may be hard to find in the lunar "sand." Such is the fate of the speculator.

Yet, even though my quantities may be whole orders of magnitude erroneous (either way!), the facts remain that these elements are present in meteorites on earth, that the same type of meteors that strike the earth also strike the moon, and that modern methods and prospecting tools befitting a lunar technology ought to be able to locate and harvest them, even if pulverized. Resistivity logging devices will yield information on porosity and, possibly, the presence of water; Geiger counters and scintilloscopes can identify subsurface rocks; magnetometers may be used to locate ferrous ore; electro-magnetometers, and similar new devices that induce polarization, can spot areas where high electrical conductivity indicates a mineral deposit; geophones used for seismic exploration on earth can reveal "geothermal" sources for the underground power plant described; nuclear spectroscopic methods should reveal data on lithology and mineralization; and a space-suited geologist with hammer and chisel ought to find enough usable materials on the first trip to justify further exploration—even if he left his mine detector home.

Unfortunately, our knowledge of meteorites will remain terribly limited if we continue to sit only on the earth—primarily because few meteors are large enough to survive the friction of our atmosphere, but also because our earth is chemically and dynamically active—eroding, transforming, and obscuring the extraterrestrial bodies that have fallen. In the entire history of mankind only 700 meteorites whose fall was observed, and only another 900 whose fall was unwitnessed, have been collected and catalogued prior to the recent NASA-sponsored searches in the last year or two!

Then too, while meteors have been plunging into our atmosphere for billions of years, scientists have been willing to acknowledge their unearthly origin only since 1803, and so our searching time has been brief and our searchers few. To make matters worse, until little over a decade ago meteorites were studied almost exclusively by mineralogists; the valuable contributions of geochemists and nuclear physicists in studying these missiles from space have been extremely recent.

The first real breakthrough in the study of meteorites will have to wait until selenographers go to the moon and study the distribution and composition of samples by the tens of thousands. Yet even then it will be as though we are a colony of semi-intelligent ants in a great wood trying to determine the origin of passing mammals and birds from their droppings. We would note similarities and differences in color, composition, and age. And there would be as many opinions as to the origin of these useful materials as there were observers of them. But in the meantime, since we would have such high-grade manure in abundance, we would use it to fertilize our fields and fire our furnaces.

Similarly, we need not wait to discover the origins of meteorites before we can melt the iron-nickels, heat the carbonaceous chondrites for their water content, and, with volcanic sulfur, mortar billion-year-old cosmic bricks together to build our underground homes.

Even as this process begins, it will be hard to restrain chemists, astronomers, and geologists like Urey; Baldwin; Green; Dr. Gerard P. Kuiper, University of Arizona; Dr. Eugene M. Shoemaker, U.S. Geological Survey of NASA; Dr. Edward Anders, University of Chicago; Dr. S. Fred Singer, University of Miami; and Dr. Thomas Gold, Cornell University—moon students all—from wanting to mine little luna for a quantity far more important than ores and building blocks. These and other theorists too numerous to credit here want to mine the moon for its knowledge.

Scientists have suggested that the moon will contain, somewhere under her shallow sands, an "original surface." But will not the search for such a surface prove as ethereal as it has on earth? After all, 4.5-billion years is a long time, and the landscape is impacted, rilled, rayed, and covered with ejecta. Why, then, is it stated so often that a major scientific reason for going to the moon is to read the record of events etched upon the ancient lunar surface?

It is true that the surface of the moon has been exposed to the flux of radiation, temperature extremes that have caused faulting, ancient volcanic activity, and old and new meteoroid cratering. Yet, compared with its larger twin, the earth, it has lived a modest life indeed, and has changed hardly at all since it was formed. Two versions of the earth seem to have been created for our pleasure: the first to ruin, the second to study when we're old enough; one to withstand the ravages of mountain building, erosion, life, storms, and wars; the other bottled in vacuum—untouched, dormant, waiting in silence until man at last musters the strength and maturity to go there, for he cannot really study and compare it until he does. The moon must surely be a record of the earth, to say nothing of the earth being a lesson in development and conservation of the moon.

How were the moon, earth, and other planets in this isolated star system formed? What are the rays on the moon? How old are the meteorites, and from where do they come? What can an on-site study of the moon contribute to our knowledge of the universe?

When we were children we learned (at least I did) that the moon somehow was formed out of the proto-earth. This argument was advanced by G. H. Darwin in "The Tides," published in 1898. Before the earth had a chance to cool, long before there were oceans, monstrous tides surged in response to the sun's pull and in resonance with the free oscillations of the earth. Each of the twice daily tides grew larger than the ones before, until after some 500 years of this, a great swell was torn from the plastic earth and thrown into space. The resulting scar on the face of the earth is the greatest valley we have, and when at last the atmosphere began to condense, the rains filled this basin that now we call the Pacific Ocean.

Some geologists believe that all oceans on earth except the Pacific have floors of granite, whereas the Pacific is floored with basalt, which is the substance of the middle layer of the earth, the mantle. Further evidence exists: if the moon really were torn from the earth, it would consist of materials having the same density as the earth's crust, and would have neither the earth's iron core nor its magnetic poles. Whether a magnetic compass will work on the moon remains for someone to go there and try one. But the mean density of the moon does approximate the density of the earth's mantle—3.34 grams per cubic centimeter.

Despite all this testimony, the earth when formed must have been nothing but viscous liquid, and the enormous friction generated in this medium would have been too strong to permit resonance tides from reaching the heights necessary for tear-off. Then, too, physicists have calculated that had the moon been torn out of the earth, it would have taken more than 8-billion years to increase the day to our present 24 hours. Since a wealth of evidence shows the earth to be but 4.5-billion years old, the Pacific Ocean hypothesis of moon creation currently is disbelieved by most geologists. My survey of geologists revealed that only 3.3% accept the Pacific Ocean theory.

Thirty per cent, on the other hand, said the moon is "a small planet, meteor, or comet that was captured by the earth's gravitational pull." And the majority, 66.7%, believe the earth and moon were born nearly in contact and at the same time, but always have been separate.

Baldwin discounts the second, or captured-planet, theory accordingly:

"The whole problem oₓ the early history of the earth-moon system is in a very unsatisfactory state at present . . . The capture of a satellite late in the history of the earth would undoubtedly be a catastrophic event whose records would remain in the rocks of that era. No such record has been detected."

The third, most popular, hypothesis seems to support the case for lunar volcanism or at least for outflows of liquid magma, because it postulates a hot moon, one that even now has a liquid metallic core, albeit substantially smaller in proportion than the earth's. According to this hypothesis, the moon was formed at the same time as the earth, the other planets, and the sun, by the gradual accretion and capture of small particles from a cloud of cosmic dust.

The dust particles moved slowly together by the minute forces of relativity or pressure of light. It must have been a patient process, consuming billions of years. When more and more of this dust accumulated, it captured additional particles. Some small fraction on the outer fringes of this forming star was moving too fast to be drawn into the nucleus. Instead, it began to condense into separate spheres by a similar process. Even as they formed, these bodies revolved around the giant central mass, which was growing hotter as it became more massive. Some of these bodies became the planets. Others, forming nearby, were captured by their larger companions and became satellites.

Harold Urey, who won the Nobel Prize for the discovery of the hydrogen isotope deuterium, has studied the problem of the origin of the solar system for 15 years. Recently he proposed a model designed to account for the chemistry, metallurgy, and composition of the planets and meteorites—a model that also explains the nature of diamonds, chondrules, silicates, and metal particles that have been found in meteorites.

In the beginning, postulates Urey, the solar system consisted of a flattened disc of gases and solids rotating about the sun as far as the present orbit of Neptune. Gravitational, as well as possibly electromagnetic, forces caused much of this material to be agglomerated into objects about the size of the moon. Solids collected at the centers and the gases at the outsides.

As these gas spheres radiated energy, they contracted and caused high temperatures and pressures to be applied to the solids at the center—temperatures and pressures so intense that even diamonds were formed.

Eventually, gases were lost from the surfaces of the spheres, and a consequent reduction of pressure and cooling took place. As they solidified and their orbits were altered, some of them collided with similar objects in neighboring orbits. Others broke up, forming meteors.

This hypothesis differs sharply with those of other theorists who have sought to explain the formation of meteorites from asteroidal-sized bodies by internal radioactive heating.

Most of these theories begin with the existence of the sun, and take it from there, assuming that the sun and the other stars were formed by the accretion of cosmic dust. The dust-cloud theory is especially intriguing, for it implies that planets and their satellites may be at least as numerous as the trillions of stars since they are a natural accompaniment of star formation. If planets are commonplace, habitable planets must be proportionately commonplace, and where there are planets that can evolve life there probably is intelligence elsewhere than on earth...

But one of Europe's most distinguished astronomers, Prof. A. Dauvillier of Pic-du-Midi Observatory at the Collège de France, believes that the stars make the dust rather than the dust makes the stars. Dauvillier speaking:

"It is easy to show that the accretion of such dust is purely a figment of the imagination." His and other hypotheses of how the universe works will be explored in Chapter VI.

The diversity of opinion sketched so briefly here (there's much more!) is not meant to confuse, but to indicate the state of confusion, the state of the unknown. It underscores the scientific obligation for going to the moon where these questions may find answer.

When we begin the laborious process of radioactive dating lunar rocks, and when we put a seismograph on the moon, we will learn its age and composition. The answer will provide the first empirical, comparative evidence as to the origin of moon and earth, and should help resolve the question of how—or whether—other stars form planets and, if so, with what likely frequency of occurrence.

Among other geologic reasons for studying the moon from the moon is to determine the shape and origin of the "great lunar bulge." Radar measurements have shown that a 7,000-foot swelling exists on the side of the moon facing earth. If it proves to be a fossil tidal bulge, it means the moon once was capable of adjusting its shape to the tidal pull of the earth and they both were formed together. But if that swelling is not tidal caused, and its existence is only accidental, it would mean the moon had been formed cold and had always had a cool, strong, thick crust. In this unlikely case, it would have had to be formed at a considerable distance from the earth, or is a captured planet.

The questionnaire to geologists penetrated into other questions of basic research, asking, "What do you think the ray-like luminous formations are that run like spokes from some lunar craters?" Answers, in order of their frequency, included: material ejected from the craters by meteoroid impact; ash flows or igneous material from ancient volcanic craters; fractures from meteoroid impact; and dikes like those around Spanish Peaks in southern Colorado. On one point they all agree.

The luminous rays of the young crater Copernicus extend in every conceivable direction. They cross over most other craters and hide most — but not all — rills and other features beneath. Are they ejecta splashed out by an impacting meteoroid? Or are they fractures created by internal volcanic processes?

The vast majority of the rays must be younger than anything else on the moon because most of them cross over craters and hide rills and other features beneath.

According to the most publicized interpretation of the Ranger photographs, the place where Ranger VII landed lies directly in the path of one of these mysterious spokes stretching hundreds of miles from the great crater Copernicus, or possibly from Tycho, and so we would expect the mystery at last to be solved.

Such is not the case, and the controversy over rays, as well as craters, now rages with a velocity increased by each new interpretation of the three sets of Ranger photographs.

The "meteoroidists," led by Prof. Kuiper, chief scientific investigator of the Ranger findings, hold the rays are ejecta splashed out from impacting meteoroids, or at least are cracks or fractures emanating from them.

The "volcanoists" believe the rays to be fractures created by internal processes, with volcanic ash being strewn along the length of such fractures. In support of this more unpublicized theory is the fact that many rays are tangential to craters and that a few are known to be blocked or stopped behind low hills. Even the landing place of Ranger VII in the Sea of Clouds apparently is subject to interpretation. The volcanic school believes Ranger VII did not land close enough to a ray for its cameras to have photographed any such feature.

Rangers VIII and IX, which landed in the Sea of Tranquility and the Crater Alphonsus, respectively, have shed no new light on the question. The Surveyor series of soft-landing craft (not yet launched as of this writing) may yield information about volcanism as well as provide information about the hardness of the lunar surface, Surveyor's prime mission. On the other hand, we may have to wait until Apollo (or Voskhod) delivers men feet first on our natural satellite.

Among other riddles awaiting our arrival on the moon is the origin of those curiously sculptured siliceous glasses known as tektites. Most geologists surveyed (56%) said they believe tektites found on earth arose from the impact of meteoroids on the earth; only 24% placed their origin on the moon; 19% thought both; and 1% neither.

NASA astronomer Dr. John A. O'Keefe is among those who believe tektities originated when meteoroids crashed into the moon. He believes that matter escapes from the moon *every* time it is hit. Dr. Shoemaker, in fact, suggests that more material leaves the moon than arrives there. When these rocks and stones are deflected into space, small portions of them go into orbit around the earth, and so become miniature moons, according to O'Keefe. Gravities of the moon and sun perturb their initial elliptical orbits, causing them to graze our atmosphere. As they do, they slow down and their orbits decay and become almost circular. Then, in the rare atmosphere, a thick surface layer melts and falls off in the form of liquid drops. As the air retards the flight of these little glass bombs, they begin to fall earthward, ablating on the way down into the air-sculptured bas reliefs we put in our museums of natural science.

Other selenologists, theorizing from simulation experiments, believe tektites formed on the moon and arrived directly instead of tear-dropping in the atmosphere. Either way, however, O'Keefe believes that if tektites have a lunar origin, then the moon has a hot interior and is either a chunk of the earth or was formed at the same time.

He reasons like this: tektites have a density of about 2.4 grams per cubic centimeter, which on crystallizing would be a few tenths higher; the earth's crust and mantle under the same vacuum conditions as the moon would have respective densities of 2.8 and 3.3. Thus, not only the earth but also the moon is capable of producing a thin outer crust lighter than beneath. The only process that possibly could cause such a condition on a planetary scale is the separation of materials in a fluid magma. Hence, it was a hot moon and, probably, one that caused numerous volcanoes or other igneous rock formations.

Further, the resemblance between tektites and common earth stones is greater chemically than between tektites and meteorites, indicating that the moon is derived from the same original materials as the earth. And so, suggests O'Keefe, it must have been a part of the earth or formed at the same time.

Urey believes there is no evidence supporting this argument. He notes that the tektites collected from the Southeast Asian and Australian "tektite belt"—the ones considered by O'Keefe—have approximately the same age of 600,000 years and can be assumed to have been produced by one event. He estimates the total mass of this wide tektite field at 1,000 tons, and asks: "Does it not seem utterly incredible that a 1,000-ton or even more massive object of such fragile structure should have been accelerated from the moon . . . and have left the moon in one piece?" Equally unlikely is the process that many small objects left the moon and became agglomerated in space.

Urey suggests that "Details so difficult to explain through known terrestrial processes are not easily and certainly explained by lunar processes."

The question of tektite origin and many, many others of potentially practical consequence remain for lunar explorers to solve: comparative questions concerned with development of the earth's crust, permanency of our ocean basins, reality of a primordial grid fracture pattern or a major transcurrent faulting, how volcanic mechanisms work, the abundance of the elements, occurrence of compounds, and the origin of the solar system, to mention only a few.

How do the scientists view the unique opportunity of possibly soon being able to study these problems on the moon? Most scientists simply don't care, according to the seven surveys discussed earlier.

Of those geologists and chemists who *responded* to the questionnaires, however, almost all of them want to find answers on the moon, although only half are in a hurry and want NASA to continue or speed up its present pace.

More are optimistic about what we'll find when we get to the moon. Some 60% believe water will be found in some form, and more than half gave an unqualified, "Yes, mining could become feasible on the moon."

An important point emerged from the surveys: those scientists who, by their specialty, should know or have a stake in something are more positive in their views than those in other fields. Thus, where 51.4% of the geologists think mining could be feasible (as opposed to 29.7% who believe it could not be, and 18.9% who remained undecided)—and where 50% of the engineers agreed— only 39% of the chemists, the control group for that question, answered the same query affirmatively. Possibly more geologists and engineers are familiar with the problems of mining than are chemists, although the propriety of this conclusion is questionable.

Similarly, more scientists representing disciplines which could most obviously or most quickly benefit from a moon laboratory wanted a fast man-on-moon program. In answer to the question, "Are you in favor of a moderately fast man-on-the-moon program for NASA?", 74.1% of the vacuum specialist respondents answered "yes" for this new world of vacuum. These were followed by 65.1% engineers, who will take us there, and 61.9% astronomers, who need an airless, steady place in space to see the stars. The middle range was upheld by chemists (53.9%) and geologists (50%). Biologists, recognizing the moon as barren of life, and apparently mostly ignoring the moon as a Cape Kennedy to Mars and Venus, scored only 46.2%, yes, less than half.

It seems that in spite of the growing interdisciplinary nature of science today; in spite of "horizontal" professional societies, magazines, and university courses; in spite of balanced project teams of synthesized scientists . . . despite all of these forces promoting the broad view, the typical scientist today remains insular.

Perhaps new knowledge emanating from the space program, if not the increasing demands upon all sciences to contribute to any given project, will promote the emergence once again of the complete scientist-engineer, the Benjamin Franklin of the 20th Century. It will take this type of person to make a success of lunar exploration, and it will take lunar exploration to make very many of these scientists.

Chapter **5**

WITNESS:

WHEREAS, the National Aeronautics & Space Act of 1958 and subsequent U.S. decisions have been made to expend great sums for the exploration of space, with the specific goal of a manned landing on the moon by 1970; and

WHEREAS, the effort to go to the moon is the most complex engineering project in history, continuously producing a wealth of new and potentially practical scientific knowledge; and

WHEREAS, the competition, opportunity for conquest, excitement, and massive stimulation of the economy engendered by the space effort can substitute for the reasons for war;

NOW, THEREFORE, the following explanations are presented on how and why space science and engineering knowledge can be transferred profitably into the industrial and social sectors of our lives.

(TIME ESTIMATE for implementing the transfer of space technology: now.)

the case for
technological transfer

THE MOON PROGRAM, as the standard bearer and stimulus of the great space effort, is the largest and most important industrial research and civil engineering project in history, far surpassing the development of the atomic bomb or construction of the pyramids. It has the potential of achieving breakthroughs in every sphere of human knowledge. If we can but learn to transfer this vast body of technology efficiently, we can inject an enormous shot of adrenalin into the business of developing new products, processes, and industrial and medical techniques. That and much, much more . . .

The premise of the case to be made for technological transfer is that even if we were not to use the moon for *anything,* the trip itself would be more than worth the cost in terms of practical knowledge learned and applied. Technological transfer is the deliberate utilization of moon-and-space-earned knowledge in the nonspace industries of earth. Of all the cases for going to the moon, this byproduct reason could well be the most important in this century. For the earthbound application of space science can be channeled into solving the serious industrial and social problems that gnaw at this civilization even as it progresses toward the stars.

Even the minor efforts made so far to adapt space technology to industrial uses already have been advantageous. But as we learn to play it, "transfer" can become a dominant theme in our technological economy and a major reason for going to the moon and beyond.

Technological transfer is not necessary to sustain the space effort any more than the space effort is necessary to eliminate war. But just as the space program satisfies some of the reasons for war, thereby making war less attractive (as will be argued later in this chapter), technological transfer is an important means of sustaining the space program. More than that, it should and can contribute to maintaining or increasing our national rate of economic growth.

Throughout this chapter I deliberately avoid the words "spinoff," "spillover," and "fallout" because they are incomplete: they imply a non-directed utilization of space accomplishments for industrial or commercial purposes, a casual benefit to be exploited if and when the transfer falls into your lap.

Unfortunately, the utilization of space technology byproducts is rarely a natural and never an accidental occurrence. Many companies possessed of truly obvious and natural byproducts of their own businesses take years or even decades to exploit them profitably. Unfamiliar space-earned byproducts, much less new scientific knowledge, concepts, and whole technologies, are not transferred automatically — not by a long shot. It takes work and effort to transfer products and ideas; few come ready made.

Nor is all space R&D of value. How much of that $20-billion allocated to land the first pair of men on the moon will go for writing proposals, attending symposiums, serving on committees, or other not directly productive work? Or purchasing, public relations, business planning, or other management operations? What portion is applicable only to the propulsion, low gravity, or vacuum conditions of space, and cannot be transferred to terrestrial industry?

The latter question may not be answerable, because in addition to tangible products that are shunted directly to industrial usage, there are thought processes, techniques, and methods of research success that are being assimilated continuously into the industrial sector. Innovation is an elusive quantity and is passed along in a variety of unnoticed ways.

Economists, technical men, and other observers of the space scene are sharply divided on the byproduct value of our enormous expenditures for space. Some feel there is a top-heavy investment of R&D effort in space projects that so far has produced little commercially useful technology.

Two of the seven surveys mentioned in previous chapters measured the attitudes of chemists and engineers involved in a broad spectrum of industrial-, government-, and university-funded research and development. A thousand engineers were selected at random from the 70,000 circulation of *Industrial Research* and sent a detailed questionnaire. An additional thousand chemists were chosen from the same list and sent a similar questionnaire.

Almost all, or 94.5%, of the engineers reported that their companies were engaged actively in at least one phase of the space program. This contrasted with only 36.4% of the chemists whose companies were so involved.

It should be noted here that chemists and chemical companies provide a singular group in the funding of R&D. Unlike the aircraft, electrical, electronic, instruments, machinery, and most other industries, the chemical and process industries pay for the vast majority of the R&D they do out of their own funds, and in this sense are not dependent upon the government. The two groups studied — engineers in companies doing space-related work and chemists in companies doing non-space-related work — may be compared as to their attitudes toward the transfer of space technology.

A little over half, or 51.9%, of engineers and only 24.5% of chemists said that there are civilian by-products of space research — transfers into either scientific or product developments — generated or used by their companies.

Less than half, or 48.2% of engineers, as compared with 39.8% of the mostly non-space oriented chemists, said that they have *heard about* industrial or consumer byproducts of space research performed by companies or organizations other than their own.

True to course, 62.6% of the engineers said they believe that one of the major benefits of the space effort will be the attainment of non-space-related developments, products, or scientific discoveries. This compared with 53.3% of the chemists who so believe in the potential of technological transfer.

Similarly, 80.5% of engineers and 72.3% of chemists believe the non-aerospace industries are benefiting from the government's heavy spending on space. Finally, 65.1% of engineers and 53.9% of chemists reported that they are in favor of a moderately fast man-on-the-moon-program for NASA.

The high percentages of affirmative answers to all these questions, and the examples the respondents furnished, diminish the charge made by transfer skeptics that few if any space projects have generated commercial products and processes. Rather, they support and overwhelmingly amplify the many recent studies of specific technological transplants made by the NASA

Office of Technological Utilization, the Department of Defense, Atomic Energy Commission, Midwest Research Institute in Kansas City, University of Denver Research Institute, Indiana University, and other universities, research institutes, and government agencies.

Both groups polled were requested to relate examples of transfer projects in their own companies or others of which they had knowledge. The examples to be described were drawn from these sources as well as from university and research institute transfer study reports. Far from complete, they were selected for their diversity and significance. They have benefited almost every industry going, and have helped create whole new industries, such as the first two categories below, the direct energy conversion industry and the cryogenics industry.

Direct energy conversion

Vanguard I, launched in March, 1958, was the first artificial earth satellite to power communications gear with *solar cells*. After the first silicon solar cells were produced at Bell Telephone Laboratories, the Semiconductor Division of Hoffman Electronics Corp., Los Angeles, took up the experimental work in 1954 and carried it through to the manufacturing stage. As a result of its willingness to risk commercial development expenses on such a "far-out" product, Hoffman sold hundreds of thousands of solar cells to Jet Propulsion Laboratory and other NASA-related organizations.

Now Hoffman and other companies involved find that a considerable quantity of less-efficient solar cells can be used in non-space devices. Portable radios can use them by the thousands; even emergency call systems for motorists stranded on superhighways and an entire telephone system in South Africa utilize solar cells today.

Thermionic and thermoelectric converters developed

by General Electric Co. as space power systems soon may find their way into commercial systems that provide electrical power at remote unattended locations. Microwave relay stations, irrigation pumping stations, weather transmitters, and navigational beacon sites easily come to mind. The source for the heat to be converted to electricity can be anything from a radioisotope to a solar heat collector, a nuclear reactor to a dish of flaming kerosene.

Cold and hot devices

Missile and space requirements for large quantities of cryogenic liquids have resulted in expanded facilities and lower prices, thus creating the new industry of low-temperature apparatus and handling. For example, Air Products & Chemicals Inc., Allentown, Pa., now is supplying *cryogenic fluids* for truck refrigeration systems and private research. Economies have been realized with *cryogenic containers*, or dewars, and now are being sold to ship liquefied methane and other hydrocarbon fuels. Still other uses include bulk storage of liquid oxygen for improved steel production, liquid nitrogen for use as a refrigerant to freeze perishable foods, and other liquefied gases for medical use.

Among countless developments in *pumps* for pumping liquid oxygen to rocket engines is one by Sundstrand's Aviation Division, Denver, that was transferred successfully to commercial jet aircraft and even an oil field application.

At the other temperature extreme, a *valve*, by Hoke Inc., Cresskill, N.J., was designed to resist alkali liquid metals in research on nuclear engines for spacecraft. Now it's being used in nuclear power stations and nonnuclear research involving high-temperature fluids.

Hot gases from the catalytic decomposition of *high-strength hydrogen peroxide* are used to power the fuel pump, the auxiliary power system, and reaction control jets on the Skyrocket, the X-15, the Mercury capsule, and other spacecraft. Concentrated peroxide also may be used soon as a source of oxygen and water for astronauts in space.

For such requirements, FMC Corp., New York, developed a 90% hydrogen peroxide solution, so strong that a rag doused in the liquid bursts spontaneously into flame. The company has learned to minimize the hazards and now is supplying the concentrated peroxide for commercial chemical manufacturing processes. It is used, for instance, in the production of insecticides and in making plasticizers and stabilizers for vinyl resins.

Instruments

Measuring the space environment in all of its many aspects has resulted in a wealth of new instruments, *most* of which have direct applications to non-space scientific problems.

Probably the best example — one that bridges the seemingly vast distance between micrometeor analysis and vaccine manufacture — is the transplant of a transducer from spaceship to bird embryo. It has become a classic example of tangible product transfer.

The original concept was developed in 1963 by Dr. Vernon L. Rogallo at NASA's Ames Research Center, Moffett Field, Cal. He arranged a pair of *piezoelectric beams* to detect the impact of micrometeors upon spacecraft and satellites. The resulting transducer was extraordinarily sensitive: it could detect an impact a thousandth of that generated by a single grain of table salt falling a distance of one centimeter!

As it turned out, the development was shelved and simpler methods used for satellite meteor detection. But an Ames physiologist familiar with the Food & Drug Administration problem of studying the effect of drugs on developing chick embryos suggested Rogallo's

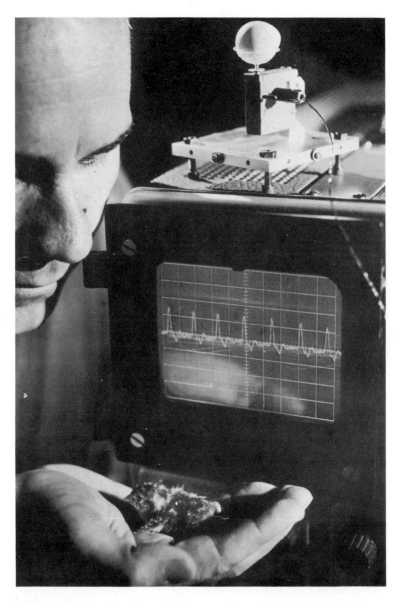

First devised to detect micrometeors, this NASA Ames Research Center device (on top of the oscilloscope) can detect the heartbeat in an egg as early as four days after it is laid. (Newly hatched bobwhite quail in experimenter's hand dominates the picture for reasons known only to the photographer.)

device as a ballistocardiograph — a device to measure the amount of blood passing through the heart in a specified time by recording recoil movements resulting from contractions.

The extreme sensitivity of Rogallo's transducer, so applied, can detect life in an egg as early as four days after it's laid. Changes in heart-beat rate and intensity resulting from temperature changes or other external stimuli also can be picked up by the instrument. Now bio-scientists have a valuable tool in such areas as vaccine production and drug research — as a result of micrometeor detection!

The Straindyne Engineering Co., Los Altos, Cal., recently began manufacturing such piezoelectric momentum transducers. The activity may provide the stimulus for finding other uses for this method of measuring minute forces.

Another unique transducer was developed by The Boeing Co. to measure structural deflections excited by complex vibrations in spacecraft. Because the sensitive element of this transducer is a *strain gage,* the output signal is directly proportional to the amplitude of vibration to which it is subjected. The transducer is well suited to high-temperature operation (to 900 F). Without modification, it can be calibrated to transduce low frequency and steady state acceleration.

Boeing estimates that production costs may be lower than conventional acceleration transducers. Thus the instrument can be used in structural testing of turbine engines or automobiles.

Honeywell's Denver Division improved its *direct writing oscillographs* as a result of their use in the space program. Reliability was greatly improved; automatic features were added to give ease and flexibility of operation; the capability of immediate review of data has been added. Commercial applications abound for such improved oscillographs in the automotive, equipment,

After direct-writing oscillographs were made more reliable and more automatic as a result of their use in monitoring telemetered information from space vehicles, they found their way into a myriad of industrial applications. This Honeywell oscillograph is sensing and recording stresses and strains from a large rolling mill at Allis-Chalmers' Milwaukee plant. Strain gages placed at various points on the rolling mill are connected to a transmitter. Its signals are received through the antenna and subsequently recorded, several channels at once, in the oscillograph.

electric motor, and household appliance industries.

The Librascope Division of General Precision Inc., Glendale, Cal., developed a technique for producing multilayer *dielectric interference filters* for missile and spacecraft tracking in order to reduce background interference and allow only the rocket flame to be seen through the filter.

These filters can be transferred to chemical process control where a property called "selective absorption" can be used. White light passing through a transparent medium is absorbed in a quantity that varies progressively with the radiation frequency. Certain frequency ranges are absorbed in an amount out of all proportion to adjacent frequency; in other words, by selective absorption.

A filter designed to pass a certain frequency can be used to monitor the amount of light selectively absorbed in that frequency range and, hence, the concentration of the chemical being monitored.

The technique has been adapted for an unusual application. It can replace the old method of "egg candling," since federal laws prevent the sale of eggs containing blood spots that exceed a certain minimum size. By comparing light passed through an egg absorbed at 5,000, 5,500, and 6,000 angstroms — using interference filters designed to pass light at each of these frequencies — the machine can spot and sort eggs that contain the too-large blood spots.

Not all good-idea instruments can be transferred, of course. An "invention without an industrial necessity" seems to describe the razor-blade *black body reference* developed at Ames Research Center.

The reference was devised as a comparison in the selection of materials for use in space, because it is necessary to measure the change in emissivity of various surfaces when exposed to actual space flight conditions over a long period of time. Ames researchers stacked razor blades together to form hills and valleys, thus causing incident radiation to be reflected from wall to wall of each valley a number of times before being reflected outward. Because of the large number of reflections, any change in emissivity of the individual surfaces has only a very small effect on the overall emissivity of the reference surface. Thus this surface has a nearly constant emissivity even though the condition of individual surfaces might change in the environment of space. (See photograph, page 138.)

The razor blade edges are blackened and stacked side by side across a copper disc to form an assembly about ¾-inch in diameter. The black body equilibrium temperature is determined by thermistors mounted in the middle of the copper base.

Black bodies are used by many industrial laboratories as reference devices, especially in spectroscopy. Types now in use are bulky, whereas the Ames device is small and compact. Should an industrial need arise for a portable instrument of this type, the razor-blade device will find a commercial home. Many space products exist in such limbo.

The wheelchair of the future (shown below) may result from an interesting contraption designed by NASA as an instrument carrier for unmanned exploration of the moon. The six-legged mechanical grasshopper, slightly modified, would make a zealous wheel-

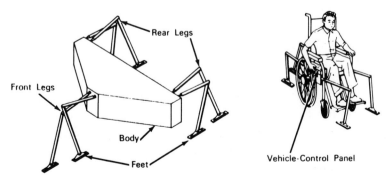

Rear Legs

Front Legs

Body

Feet

Vehicle-Control Panel

chair that could traverse sand, street curbs, and rough ground without assistance. It also could be controlled remotely and used for civil defense operations, rescue work, and to detect land mines.

Components

Electronic and mechanical components have increased in sophistication and quantity as a result of space research.

For example, a *connector* that joins the circuit between two printed circuit boards without solder was developed by Brown Engineering Co. Inc., Huntsville, Ala., to withstand great vibration, permit dense packaging, and insure reliability for space vehicles. The connectors now are being transferred for use in digital computers.

A *photo-dielectric tape* representing a new type of image-sensing device for space vehicles is under development at RCA's Astro-Electronics Division in Hightstown, N.J. Because an optical image is stored by converting it into an electronic charge pattern that can be read out directly as a video signal by an electron beam, the system has an inherently high resolution. The system also can expand the useful part of the radiation spectrum, giving better sensitivity than standard photographic or television techniques. Its high resolution properties render the tape ideally suited for use in analog or digital data handling or processing systems.

Hughes Aircraft Co., Fullerton, Cal., developed a small, lightweight *cathode ray tube display* to give an astronaut in space information from his instruments without necessitating undue movement on his part. Astronauts often find themselves in cramped, restricted postures due to the small size of their spaceships, zero gravity, or high vibration, and find it difficult to monitor their instruments.

An answer to this problem, called "Electrocular," consists of a one-inch-diameter cathode ray tube, a single front surface mirror, an adjustable focusing lens, and a reflecting eyepiece — all mounted on a headband. The whole thing weighs only 30 ounces on earth, and with the viewing eyepiece positioned in front of one eye, presents the observer with a monocular virtual image of the display information superimposed on the surrounding background.

Non-space applications? Galore. Naval officers, for instance, need not return to the fleet's display center to obtain revised visual briefings during rapidly changing battle or storm conditions. Pilots could divide their attention between watching their instruments and viewing the airborne traffic pattern ahead.

In industry, assembly workers wearing electrocular devices could receive instructions on wiring and installing components in complex systems, eliminating blueprints or printed instructions. Engineers who have to adjust equipment by consulting instruments beyond their area of vision would find the device a distinct aid. In medicine, it could help a surgeon instantly detect any change in the patient's pulse or respiration rate.

Another component worthy of widespread transfer to the commercial sector of the economy is ITT Federal Laboratories' *electronic scanning star tracker.* This division of International Telephone & Telegraph used a special multiplier phototube to eliminate problems inherent in conventional star trackers for space vehicles. These problems include having to make allowances for lubricant evaporation in rotating star trackers, expending additional energy to remove the angular momentum given to a vehicle by a rotating device, and vibration generated by the scanning rotor.

The non-rotating device avoids these problems. Moreover, the phototube can be transferred to applications such as celestial tracking in ship navigation and

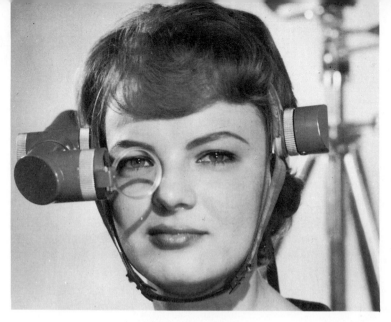

Small cathode ray tube and eyepiece device first was designed for astronauts to receive visual information in cramped spaceships. Now similar Hughes Aircraft headsets are used in industry and medicine by workers who find it convenient or essential to keep their eyes on the job. In airport control tower, below, wearer receives radar display or other air traffic data while moving about freely to perform various tasks.

utilization of the tracker's high electro-optical sensory accuracy in automated servo control systems such as are used with milling machines.

Computers

Among a wealth of computer systems devised originally for space vehicles — in this case for the X-15 rocketship and the Air Force X-20 Dyna-Soar manned space glider — is Honeywell's *self adaptive autopilot.* It is a computer that adapts automatically to compensate for varying flight conditions such as altitude, speed, and weight.

Directly transferring this rocketship technology to light twin-engine aircraft, Honeywell scientists felt that "a whale had spawned a minnow." The minnow-sized commercial adaptive autopilot reduces the possibility of pilot error and makes small craft flying significantly safer by adapting to unforeseen flight conditions.

Another piece of space computer work resulted in the Instrumentation DIgital On-line Transcriber by North American's Rocketdyne Division, Canoga Park, Cal. The "IDIOT" is smarter than its acronym: it converts *analog data to digital input data.* It samples 100 input channels at 10,000 measurements per second, thereby saving a tremendous amount of time in analyzing test information. Devised first to simplify rocket engine test work, the company currently is licensing IDIOT for commercial sales. Digitizing of analog data is done frequently in a wide range of engineering and research fields.

A number of exotic methods of putting things together have come out of the complex requirements of space components. Probably the most important is the *electron beam process* which, although it was patented in 1907, came into widespread use only when the space requirement arose for high-quality welds and machining techniques otherwise unattainable. Electron beaming, in which electrons emitted from a cathode are accelerated to the speed of light to provide energy, now is used in industry to weld porous tungsten or thick aluminum, to join dissimilar materials, or for surface planing, contour cutting, and piercing.

Fabrication methods

The little explored *laser welding*—in which a coherent beam of light is concentrated in a small area — also shows promise, having been spurred by space needs. Unlike the electron beam, the laser requires no vacuum and there is no secondary radiation hazard.

Chemical milling — an old process used to remove metal at a uniform, controlled rate to change the shape of metal parts — was improved by North American Aviation Inc. to produce a lightweight rocket casing. One of North American's subsidiaries, Navan Products Inc., then extended its application to the automotive industry. Turco Products Inc., Wilmington, Cal., also did original work in the field and now licenses the process to every major American aircraft manufacturer, which use it to "chem-mill" airframes of commercial airplanes. Parts for certain types of office equipment also can be refined with the process.

Explosive metal forming, using cheap dies sometimes made of ice reinforced with shredded paper, and *magnetic pulse forming*, where an intense magnetic field is used to force metal to expand against dies, are other fabrication techniques devised to produce complex space components. They are used widely now by companies engaged in sheet metal forming, tank-end forming, tube forming, hole punching, and marine vessel and automotive manufacture. For parts that have swaged fittings, magnetic forming shrinks the metal with less spring-back than any other method and gives a stronger, safer joint.

Solid state bonding was originated by National Research Corp., Cambridge, Mass., when a contractual NASA job called for the prevention of metals from bonding to one another in space. At room temperature in vacuum, pieces of mild steel stick to each other so tightly that it takes force a fifth as great to break the joint as to break the steel itself. At 500 C, vacuum joints are virtually *as strong as* the steel.

The job at hand was to prevent the bonding in vacuum. But it is easy to see how the knowledge gained in this research could be transferred directly to devise methods for joining metal parts, for instance in manufacturing electronic components. If perfected, such a technique would have the advantage of retaining the desirable electrical and physical characteristics of the bulk metal in the joint. (See pictures, page 29.)

Materials

Among the scores of new and improved materials designed for the high strength-to-weight and everything-resistant needs of spacecraft and components, few have been more profitable than *maraging steels* (so called because their *martensitic* structure is *age*-hardened). International Nickel Co. did not develop maraging steels originally for space use, but the space age certainly accelerated their development by providing an immediate market for large thin-gage pressure vessels such as the skin of solid propellant missiles and experimental rocket cases. Following Inco's developments in its Bayonne Research Laboratories in New Jersey and a joint Inco-NASA program at Lewis Research Center to devise spacecraft testing methods, thousands of tons have been produced for non-space markets.

The maraging steels are almost completely carbon-free and contain from 18 to 25% nickel as well as other alloying agents. Since they attain yield strengths of

"Maraging" steel, containing 18% nickel and other alloying agents, was improved by International Nickel and NASA for rocket motor casings. Today, pressure vessels, hydrofoils, and low-distortion gun parts are made of this extremely high-strength steel. Picture shows test firing of huge Lockheed 156-inch diameter solid propellant rocket motor, in which 1-million pounds of thrust are unleashed.

250,000 to 300,000 pounds per square inch, they naturally found first use in large rocket motor cases and, now, solid propellant boosters. Large pressure vessels, low-distortion gun parts, and hydrofoils are non-space applications where the low distortion and high strength of maraging steels excel.

The demand for higher performance in rocket motor components has led to the development at Lewis of a whole class of nickel-base alloys that stay strong up to 1800 F and higher. These alloys, containing molybdenum, chromium, aluminum, and of course nickel, were designed to withstand high heat and stress in spacecraft structural castings and as outer panels of re-entry vehicles. Now they are used almost routinely in many commercial engines for turbine buckets, rotors, combustion liners, and structural members.

The *vacuum-aluminized polyester* skin of the Echo satellite, only 0.5 thousandth of an inch thick, was supplied by G. T. Schjeldahl Co. It made the big satellite highly reflective without adding much weight. Later, National Research Corp. found a similar film to be a super-insulation, the best so far discovered for extremely low temperatures. When crinkled around the object to be insulated, it creates thousands of tiny cells that minimize radial heat conduction. Dr. Milo P. Hnilicka, NRC chief scientist who developed the material, once told me he made a sleeping bag out of the thin material and slept warmly in sub-zero weather.

NRC has patented the insulation, and has licensed Standard Steel to use it on large tanks and Hofman-Paul Cryogenics Division of Air Reduction Co. Inc. to use it on laboratory dewars.

One more example from among the dozens of space materials will suffice to demonstrate that materials, as much or more than anything else, have bridged the sometimes-easy, sometimes-difficult gulf from spaceship to industrial furnace. Early in 1958, General Electric

Pyrolytic graphite, above, is a space-developed material that has found its way from spaceship nose cones to refractory furnace linings and high-temperature electronic components. Blast from 6700 F butane torch is withstood by the material at left, while similar blast at right burns hole through asbestos. Below, black-body reference surface composed of razor-blade edges provides a more portable instrument. So far, device is a space invention seeking an industrial necessity.

began investigating techniques for making large free-standing shapes of *pyrolytic graphite* for use as nose-cones. Pyrolytic graphite, produced by depositing carbon in vapor phase onto a substrate, possesses a high degree of anisotropy; that is, its physical, electrical, and thermal properties in one plane differ substantially from the same properties in a perpendicular plane. The research was successful and it worked well as a thermal shield or rocket nozzle.

Now, "transfer research" is underway to develop it for uses requiring thermally or chemically resistant refractory materials such as furnace parts, piping, or crucibles for coating molten metals or caustic solutions. Other applications exist in electronics: as frequency filters, thermistors, high-temperature capacitors, and variable fuses. The work continues not only at GE, but also at Lockheed, High Temperature Materials Inc., Union Carbide Corp., and Raytheon Co.

The list of transfers from space work goes on and on. It includes plasmajets devised for re-entry simulation and used now to vaporize even refractory materials. It includes the entire field of telemetry and communications, where absolutely reliable communications with space vehicles became the need that spawned whole generations of radio antennas, transmitters, receivers, and specialized data handling equipment that have passed into commercial fields. Medical technology has advanced rapidly through space programs ranging from contributions in improved medical examinations to electronic instrumentation. Vibrational testing, packaging and shipping — and even management and control methods — have benefited from space emphasis. For instance, the now widely used PERT (Program Evaluation and Review Technique) method was an outgrowth of the sheer complexity of the Navy's Polaris project.

All these and many hundreds of other more or less

tangible product transfers have come from the space effort. Still others have resulted from missile, weapon, and other governmental and defense R&D programs.

Information transfers, however, although difficult to track down, are even more lucrative to the commercial sector of our economy. Whereas "product transfer" involves well-developed devices, processes, or materials originally conceived for space-related applications, "information transfer" is considerably less tangible.

A few examples of information transfer will be attempted, but by definition the flow of knowledge from space project to industry is not as direct or as smooth as may appear below:

The entire field of silicon semiconductors would be nowhere near the advanced state of development today if it were not for the stringent reliability requirements of the space market. Information acquired as a NASA supplier is not forgotten when the manufacturer produces industrial components, as witness Texas Instruments Inc., Westinghouse, and other large space-and-commercial vendors. As a byproduct of high space standards of reliability, for instance, Westinghouse recently was able to offer a lifetime guarantee on commercial silicon power transistors.

At Sprague Electric Co., North Adams, Mass., reliability of the company's solid tantalum capacitor was increased five-fold to meet space requirements. The improved techniques and processes now are utilized in the production of hearing aids, medical instrumentation, aircraft control systems, and miniature transistor radios.

Knowledge of solid state physics and printed circuitry gained from its participation in space programs enabled Allied Research Associates Inc., Boston, to develop a device that automatically sorts cigars for uniformity of color.

At the Avco-Everett Research Laboratory in Everett, Mass., the study of spacecraft re-entry problems developed a theoretical understanding of the electrical conductivity characteristics of gases at high temperatures. The information could have application in the large-scale generation of electric energy using magnetohydrodynamic principles. A real advantage of such a plant would be the much higher thermal efficiencies inherent in MHD power—nearly 60% as compared with the current 40% maximum.

Astronauts who remain in orbit for extended periods may be unable to endure the effects of weightlessness upon the cardiovascular system without artificial gravity. Douglas, Lockheed, and other companies are studying the problem. Several partial simulation programs, using centrifuges and pressure suits underwater, are generating human performance data applicable to deep-sea systems as well as to automobile and airplane crash survival devices. (See pictures, pages 214-15.)

Most groups that have studied the problem of technology transfer agree that information transfer is a far more vital economic commodity than the mere passage of space products to commercial use. Economic benefits are hard to measure here, for we are talking now not about borrowing pyrolytic graphite nose cones for our furnace components, but about the perplexing and fantastically complex problem of information retrieval and *usage*. Using the knowledge that surrounds us is the unique problem of our dynamic age, the tremendous problem of our success. It is the admission that we have an entirely new natural resource, one so significant as to reduce the relative importance of physical resources —the almost untapped natural resource of new knowledge.

Right or wrong, the decision to land U.S. citizens on the moon by 1970 has been made. From now until then, expenditures for all types of governmental, industrial, and university R&D each year will increase from $21-billion to $30-billion, with the moon and space projects consuming about 20% of the total. Considering those sums, for how much should we insure our space program to stimulate industrial expansion? Should we pay a normal 2% annual insurance premium (some $84-million, based on 20% of the 1965 R&D budget)? Or $10-million? Few would argue against allocating *something* to assure the industrial byproduct of space.

NASA currently is spending about $3-million a year for the job. It goes into extensive data storages, publications, and technology utilization centers. But despite a good start with product transfers, NASA finds it difficult to *communicate* — as opposed merely to collect, preach, and publish — useful scientific information relating to no specific product or technique. The building of corporate capabilities and facilities should be the goal of information transfer. But since this knowledge does not come packaged ready for delivery from space lab to industrial lab, a management barrier exists, and it is formidable.

Most of the work so far has been directed toward product transfers because they are the easiest to explain and the most readily accepted. Unfortunately, potential utilizers of intangible information transfers have come to expect that ideas suggested by NASA are tangible products, pre-wrapped and ready for assembly line.

An unfortunate signal has been established: one of those mysterious codes so prevalent in our economy seems to have evolved all by itself. It is analogous to the use of narrow-necked bottles for catsup and wide ones for mustard. As far as I know, no collusion exists between condiment manufacturers and consumers, but the shapes of those bottles have become a reliable signal to the housewife. Industry leaders somehow believe that reports that are bylined NASA come only in narrow-necked bottles.

Yet, only since NASA has been in business has any effort been made to stimulate industry's awareness of information transfer. It is precisely those who deplore the money being "wasted" for space who are abysmally unaware of the governmental sources of transfer information. Ignorance or narrow-bottle attitudes may prevent many managements from "receiving" NASA suggestions, but the space agency is "sending" — in quantity.

For instance, *Scientific & Technical Aerospace Reports (STAR)*, published by NASA, Washington, D.C., abstracts current information of new aerospace findings. *International Aerospace Abstracts*, published by the American Institute of Aeronautics & Astronautics, Phillipsburg, N.J., puts in one place a wealth of information from many magazines. Both are available every other week for a moderate annual subscription. *NASA Tech Briefs* also are issued periodically to acquaint industry with the technical content of innovations derived from the space program. And English translations of important Russian advances are available from NASA for a few dollars.

In addition, independent scientific and professional magazines, such as *Industrial Research*, Industrial Research Bldg., Beverly Shores, Ind., now departmentalize news of space developments that have application to industry.

Although 50 reports on the ionosphere of Mars probably are issued for every one on the welding of aluminum, both types are packed with new findings relating to practical science and, therefore, to industry. These reports and other informational activities of utilization specialists within NASA and cooperating universities presuppose that industry leaders can read. That is, that they are willing to swallow, digest, and then profitably apply this wealth of biweekly input.

Experience has shown that they are not. Most companies advance technically by the centimeter. They readily apply Hamilton-Standard water-cooled underwear for Apollo astronauts to water-cooled underwear for a racecar driver in the "Firecracker 400," but they rarely seize upon a space-developed understanding of, say, energy conversion, master the information, and then apply it to developing entirely new products or services.

Why?

I used to believe the answer lies in the supposition that not enough managements are technically oriented. But since then I have seen too many technical as well as non-technical managements hard at work committing sins of omission: they do not read sufficiently beyond their immediate interests. They do not seek ideas. Or, having idea men on their payrolls, they listen but fail to act. Often they are alert to new technologies, but not to new technological markets.

I believe the problem is not that entrepreneurs are not engineers, but that they are not entrepreneurs! They are simply managers, controllers, keepers of the status quo.

Entrepreneurs, conversely, are supposed to create opportunities and initiate change. Either may lack the knowledge of technology, but the entrepreneur makes it his business to find out in such a way that he can extend his company's involvement, capability, and profit. His job is to take calculated risks. He views his job as an effort to obsolete something—preferably his competitors' products!

A real entrepreneur should be as much an artist with his observations of technology and markets as is an architect with his observations of the honeycomb structure of a beehive or the meander of a stream. All artists transfer from nature and from disciplines other than their own. Technological transfer, after all, is only a profit extension of that art.

It may be as futile to ask why we have entrepreneurs who are afraid to take risks as it is to consider why we have architects who can't design, salesmen who can't sell, or scientists who can't invent. Few people who possess the latent talent are willing to invest the necessary years of application and self discipline. As Victor Hugo once said, "People do not lack strength, they lack will."

All causes of non-creativity cannot be explained that easily. It seems clear, though, that one cause of lustless management is our national hypersecurity. A languor is growing in this so-rich society that automatically supplies too many human needs, allowing controllers instead of leaders to rise by default to positions of corporate leadership and discouraging risk-taking because, although less profitable, it is considerably more comfortable to play it safe. By contrast, the observation has been made, perhaps deservedly, that foreign-born Americans, having been bred in a more hostile environment, surpass the natives in starting new U.S. enterprises.

Solutions to juiceless leadership are beginning to be discussed at many levels of our society, adding emphasis to the gravity of the problem. For instance, Midwest Research Institute, to which NASA gave the job of conducting a pilot effort to speed up the commercial applications of space technology, believes that social scientists are needed as intermediaries and as salesmen. The technically aware sociologist or psychologist, working at the interface between space developments and commercial enterprise, would help the industrial leader get his attitudes in order to accept the benefits of technological transfer, much as a computer specialist helps his client organize data for programing. The big problem, according to these transfer specialists, is getting the company president to realize he has a problem.

"I have no problems," said the typical president, "except my ulcer!"

In an experiment to influence tomorrow's industrial leaders at a pre-ulcer stage, Midwest Research Institute, Trans World Airlines, and the University of Missouri at Kansas City, under a NASA contract, are studying the feasibility of special training programs. They would condition industrial executives to an awareness of how to adapt the new technology to their specific corporate objectives. Such "schools for entrepreneurship" could be located within professional schools, probably the business schools of concerned universities. MRI president Charles Kimball suggests that "some university is going to make a name for itself by leading with such a program."

It is intriguing that all serious attempts to get the most for our space money end up by concerning themselves with changing the attitudes of management, educational expansions, and other techniques of psychological therapy. Philosophers long have deplored the over-emphasis on technology to the detriment of social progress; now it seems that the former can spur the latter. The idea is akin to the biochemist's hope of curing mental illness with drugs — an avoidance of how the patient got that way in trade for a direct attack on the problem of making him function healthily. So may it be with our social illnesses.

Urban decay, unemployment, air and water pollution are the least of these. There is a far more important and complex goal. The moon project may be large enough to have byproduct potential far surpassing ordinary technological and social contributions. It may qualify as a substitute for war.

All of us living in this or any earlier generation on the earth have been affected by war. Who has not in these generations thought at one time or another about the abolition of war, envisioning the eradication of that social disease somewhat as typhus has been eradicated by knowledge and tenacity? But where the bacillus causing typhus first had to be discovered, the causes of war are well known. War is caused by any one or more of the following overt, covert, real, or imagined desires of leaders or parts of their populations:

1. For conquest; that is, to steal — land, products, or people — adding to the wealth of the victor.

2. To steer the attention of a nation's 'own populace away from internal problems, thereby lengthening the leaders' tenure of power.

3. To impose one group's culture, language, religion, or ideology on another group.

4. For competition through demonstrations' of power and capability.

5. To focus attention on a national goal that will help unify and solidify the nation.

6. For excitement, adventure, and danger.

7. To provide a reason for constructing and destroying products on a massive scale in order to stimulate the economy.

8. To satisfy a psychotic death wish extended to include many lives or even all life on earth.

Viewed as desires of government to be accomplished without killing people, the first three of these activities still are immoral: they involve stealing, deception, and slavery, respectively. The next four are terribly expensive, but otherwise inherently harmless. The last is so far beneath what we ordinarily call immorality, yet so rooted in the other "reasons for war," that it too may be minimized by a suitable war substitute.

To think that nations even in recent comparatively enlightened centuries regularly and inevitably turn to war to satiate these desires would be unbelievable to any other-world intelligence who has not witnessed the terrible reality of war.

The strange and odious fact of war is that it works. It does add wealth to the victor; it does divert and channel the people; it is extremely effective in spreading the gospel of the conquerors; it massively stimulates the economy; it provides a national goal; and it is considerably more exciting and dangerous than a football game. Although nuclear weapons now change the odds somewhat and force national leaders to define "victor" more carefully, the crime of war does pay.

What does all this have to do with the moon and space program?

I submit that for the first time in history we have a slim chance — slim, but nevertheless a real opportunity — to eliminate war by substituting another massive endeavor, a moral one, in place of the immoral "remedy" of destructive conflict. Obviously, some fundamental changes within individual thinking are necessary to eliminate war, and the argument is not presented as a panacea for this most dominant of all human problems. War is resorted to after a nation has exhausted other alternatives. Substituting a massive space effort presents additional alternatives.

Substitution is not a great idea, merely a good one. Just as arms control can proceed slowly and need not be focused exclusively on grand plans to moralize humanity, the economic, emotional, cultural, competitive, prestigious, and other *national reasons* for going to war can be replaced slowly and thoughtfully with a great design.

Space travel with specific, logical, attainable goals — such as landing on the moon, then colonizing the moon, then landing men on the planets, etc. — may be just what we're looking for. Let's examine the eight reasons for war listed above to see how they may be satisfied by national space programs.

The potential conquests of territory in space far

exceed the puny visions of Napoleon or Hitler, who merely would conquer one world. Unlike war, which is limited in scope and territory, space travel can win us the riches of the moon and the planets, and then illimitable new worlds.

The moon program already has focused the attention of the man in the street and the political leaders. It has dominated the peacetime budget. It thus has directed the attention of the population, but has done so without the blind arrogance of a war effort. It has steered attention without necessarily hiding other problems and without perpetuating dictatorships, a danger even republics face in all-out world wars.

Similarly the space effort has helped impose the culture, language, and ideologies of the two leading spacefaring nations on the rest of earth. These cultures are imposed naturally, through leadership and the example of accomplishment, and not by force. It is one difference between morality and immorality.

Competition between the United States and the U.S.S.R. even in these infant steps into space is strong. It is marked by a mature sense of friendliness, of genuine congratulations on both sides for the scientific accomplishments of the other. Contrast this scene to the newspaper nonsense each side publishes whenever a political or warlike "accomplishment" is made.

Competition in space already has led in small instances to cooperation in space, as witness the U.S.-Soviet Union coordinated launchings of satellites to get weather data and to map the earth's magnetic field. Conceivably, both scientific competition and cooperation can lead to a rapport that will help preclude enmities. If so, maybe we can exchange technological information transfers one day on a world-wide scale instead of only nationally. It is a logical extension of the idea that engaging in trade with your potential enemy helps avoid war. In this case we would exchange space knowledge and ways to apply it. These would be substantially more dynamic ambassadors of peace than static wheat and tractors.

As far as war providing a national goal is concerned, this benefit is readily assumed by space travel, as it has been in earlier times by pyramid building and other great civil engineering projects. The people are proud of their nation's exploits. The nation is solidified, the team is united, and sportsmanship prevails as in a football game. The blessings of nationalism are achieved while the evils of nationalism are avoided. Even little Lydia and Liberia now have space programs, the purposes of which are to provide national objectives and not necessarily to replenish humanity's storehouse of knowledge.

The opportunities for excitement, adventure, and danger exist many times over in the conquest of the moon and other worlds. Space travel is inherently more exciting than war because the adventure is not spoiled by the grim knowledge that the purpose of your adventure is to destroy lives. (For those who delight in high-risk adventures, the danger of space is even more exquisite: an astronaut can die in a thousand ways, from having his blood boil in the vacuum of space to being squashed on the high-gravity surface of Jupiter.)

Skeptics may argue that spacefare is more vicarious than warfare. It is, of course, but that situation will improve with time. We have been fighting wars ever since man began to organize into groups. Space flight has just begun. More and more young men will be drawn irresistibly into the challenge of space, and they will be drawn there by choice. Most of the population will contribute to the adventure in factories and laboratories, where most people participate even in total wars.

Among all of the pressures leading to war, the desire to stimulate the economy is usually the strongest. The Orwellian idea of keeping a war going perpetually elsewhere hardly need wait until 1984 to realize its monetary reward. If economic benefit is the most compelling reason for war, it is also the most compelling reason for substituting a moonship for a fleet of ICBMs, a Cape Kennedy for a battlefield, or a massive intellectual effort for a mass production war effort.

Project Apollo is the biggest single peacetime job in history. This first of many moon projects already has employed three times as many people as did the construction of the pyramids, and their efforts are resulting in structures considerably more impressive. Consider just one — the gargantuan architectural fantasy of our major spaceport: Cape Kennedy.

Immense control booths and scores of red-painted gantry stands dot this futuristic landscape from which, on the average of once every three weeks, something is launched into space. Mobile launch towers 30 stories high and weighing 12-million pounds each are picked up routinely these days on giant crawler-transporters each half the size of a football field.

Soon, such a crawler will move its tower into a building that when finished will be several times larger than the largest in the world. It will be bigger than the Merchandise Mart and the Pentagon combined — so big that its air will have to be kept in continous motion to prevent clouds and rain from forming inside! There, the giant moon rocket, Saturn V, and its capsule and lunar vehicles will be put together late in this decade.

It will comprise but one experiment.

The resources of the two most powerful nations this planet has ever spawned are being mobilized for many such space experiments. In this country, our beneficent peacetime crash program to land men on the moon by 1970 will cost five times more than the wartime crash program to build the first atomic bomb. In all 50 of the United States, 20,000 companies are deeply committed and about 315,000 Americans are at work on various facets of the space effort.

The differences between space efforts and war efforts are all good: the economic and manpower commitment for space can be slowed or advanced and need not consume the nations that wage it; people don't get killed, at least not deliberately, and never in any great numbers; the space effort can go on forever, for it does not end in destruction and waste but in accomplishment and the extension of knowledge; the byproduct of the space effort is a flow of ideas, research projects, products, techniques, and processes from space applications to the industrial sector.

Thus, in every one of the eight reasons given for war — except one — space travel can substitute for war. The single remaining obstacle is the insanity of the men who start war. Even here, perhaps, the envisioned better society that challenges, competes, cooperates, and expends its energies on space may spawn fewer mad leaders.

When discussed against the background of current needs and events, the space effort is not "money wasted" and the transfer of space technology is more than a casual byproduct of "money spent anyway." Space and its byproduct are important tools of industry and government, of 20th Century society. The space effort, of which the trip to the moon is the first significant milestone, is right to assume that proud aura of pyramid building, with this difference: the complex journey to the moon and beyond is an unmystical, dynamic stride in the extension of human horizons.

Chapter *6*

WITNESS:

WHEREAS, the oldest of the sciences, astronomy, has been handicapped severely due to the dense and erratic atmosphere surrounding the surface of the planet earth; but

WHEREAS, the essentially airless, low gravity, and slowly rotating moon provides a place where the seeing always will be perfect, where very large mirrors and lenses can be used effectively, and where telescopes will turn almost 30 times more slowly than they do on earth; and

WHEREAS, the far side of the moon is the most easily attainable place in the solar system where terrestrial radio interference can be completely cancelled;

NOW, THEREFORE, the following arguments are offered as to why the moon should be exploited as humanity's eventual major location for seeing and hearing the earth, solar system, the stars, galaxies, and cosmic dust.

(TIME ESTIMATE for an initial manned astronomical observatory on the moon: 1980.)

the case for seeing the universe

NEW YORK CITY could be sitting on Mars and we wouldn't recognize it through a telescope on earth as anything more than an inconsequential puff of dark smoke—and then only if the smoke extended all the way to "Philadelphia." The reason we would be so oblivious of such a Martian artifact is that the resolving power of our telescopes is limited by our atmosphere. It doesn't do any good to increase magnifications further until we find a way to get the telescopes into space.

Earth's atmosphere is a veil, blotting out or distorting significant radiation emanating from the universe. Both optical and radio astronomers refer to that portion of the electromagnetic spectrum where they can receive radiation as "windows" into space. These windows are small. Too little of the ultraviolet and infrared radiation penetrates our atmosphere. Very long radio waves, longer than 20 meters, are reflected back to space by the ionosphere (see chart, pages 156-7).

Many other problems are inherent in using telescopes on earth, all of which can be eliminated by an observatory on the moon: mirrors and lenses of large telescopes sag excessively; the portion of telescope tubes near the openings of their domes cool faster than the parts farther inside, distorting the optical path; observatory domes trap warm air, funneling it to the outside where it interferes with the seeing; wet air helps corrode aluminized telescope mirrors; rain, wind, or clouds interfere; local atmospheric perturbations intrude even when the sky is cloudless; and the earth rotates too fast, necessitating constant corrections for altitude.

Add to all that the closing of optical windows in the daytime, and you can see why it does not pay to use an optical telescope on earth *most of the time.*

It is a tribute to the resourcefulness and patience of mankind that we have gathered the facts that we have from beneath our atmospheric ocean.

Fortunately, several times during the course of a year, periods of clear weather occur when the disturbed horizontal layers in the atmosphere tend to disappear. Sometimes, too, the air is dry and steady, as during a temperature inversion. In the lack of wind and temperature variations, thermal distortions of the telescope and dome also are absent. If all these conditions occur *at the same time,* and if it is night and your turn at the telescope, it may be possible to obtain a good view of celestial objects. It is at such times that astronomers have made their great discoveries.

When you stop to think about it, you realize that astronomers have an unusual research problem. There are only two big optical telescopes that can be used today on "frontier problems." These are the 120-inch reflector at the Lick Observatory on Mt. Hamilton near San Francisco and the 200-inch reflector on Mt. Palomar between Los Angeles and San Diego. (A reflector is a telescope in which the principal focusing element is a mirror; the focusing element in a refractor telescope is a lens.)

Even using these giant reflectors in simultaneous programs—for instance, working with very faint objects in the dark of the moon and doing spectroscopic work in moonlight—you find that only a handful of astronomers can participate. (This is not true of radio telescopy.)

The National Academy of Sciences' recent Panel on Astronomical Facilities said of these two big optical telescopes: "No more than two or three astronomers in the entire world . . . have the opportunity to work on the most exciting problems in any given field."

A lunar observatory would be in operation all of the time. Since an observatory on the moon would extend the time of individual astronomers to make discoveries, a lunar observatory could extend the useful lifetimes of discovery-making astronomers by a large factor.

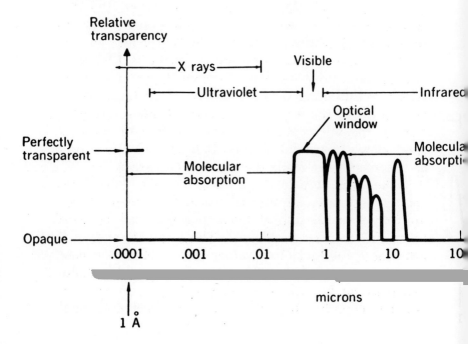

But more than that, an observatory on the moon may advance the science of astronomy (and the related knowledge of physics) more in a single decade than the previous thousands of years of observation from earth.

Why? Contrast the view from earth with this view from the moon:

The observatory is placed somewhere between the poles so that the panorama of the universe unfolds before us, but much more leisurely here since the moon rotates almost 30 times more slowly than the earth. Tracking a star from horizon to zenith is a simple matter then, and there is no need to correct for the various thicknesses of an atmosphere. (There *is* a need, however, to add an oscillating correction for a large telescope since the moon "librates," or wobbles slightly. This is one of comparatively few disadvantages of telescopy from the moon.)

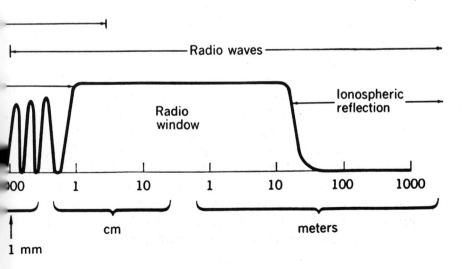

Radio waves

Radio window

Ionospheric reflection

)00   1   10   1   10   100   1000

cm   meters

1 mm

As though the 350-hour night were not long enough, the stars shine even in the daytime on the moon, and they shine steadily. We can follow many of the variable stars with accuracy through two or three cycles to determine minor changes. We can separate the images of very close double stars to measure their orbits, something that cannot be done on earth.

And we can make far better measurements of stellar parallax, for there is no drifting of the image or uncertainties arising from refraction effects. Better values of parallax are essential for understanding the distance scale of the universe.

In the low gravity and absence of atmosphere we could use a 1,000- or 2,000-inch mirror effectively, something impossible on earth. It would enable us to study at length the spectra of much fainter objects than anyone thought possible.

As the words "spectra" and its singular form "spectrum" will be used throughout this chapter, it may be of interest to explain something about how astronomers obtain and use spectra. Isaac Newton produced the first spectrum in 1666 (at the age of 23). In a darkened room, he passed a beam of sunlight from a slit in the window shade through a prism, displaying the result on the opposite wall. The "result," of course, was the separating of white light into its colored parts—the familiar rainbow we call the "spectrum," with violet on one end and red on the other. Later Newton added a lens between prism and wall to focus the spectrum sharply. This crude instrument was the first spectroscope, or instrument for analyzing the colors of light.

If you look closely at the spectrum produced by a spectroscope—as Joseph von Fraunhofer did first in 1814—you find it is not a continuous rainbow band, but is crossed by numerous dark lines of different degrees of intensity. Such "Fraunhofer lines" were found to be veritable fingerprints of the elements.

Scientists quickly began heating various elements to incandescence and making spectrograms of the light they emitted. These known spectra were compared with spectra of unknown substances. When the thousands of lines of two spectra from different sources matched perfectly, identifications could be made; when the lines of a spectrum were uncharacteristic of any known element, new elements sometimes were named. Cesium and rubidium were discovered in this way. In fact, the search for more new elements led to the spectroscopic exploration of the sun. Helium was discovered there—and it wasn't until 30 years later that helium was found on the earth.

Today, astronomers collect the light from a star or other celestial light source in a telescope and send it through a spectroscope onto a photographic plate. The instrument in such cases is more properly called a spectro*graph* because the images are recorded photo*graph*ically.

The spectrograph used in conjunction with the telescope has become the astronomer's prime tool for measuring the temperature, magnetic attractions, velocity, and many other characteristics of stars. But although this remarkable tool and its various adaptations (ultraviolet spectrometers, x-ray spectrometers, spectrophotometers, etc.) have been refined to a high degree of perfection, their use on earth still is limited by the ocean of atmosphere enveloping our planet. If we could get a spectroscope-telescope into space — or better on the moon where the environment is the same as space except for the important fact that it is a steady, stable platform — we could record spectra from many more sources than is possible on earth.

For instance, we could analyze subdwarf stars that cannot be seen from earth, "quasars" (to be explained later), and other faint objects. Perhaps we even will discover planets attending the nearer stars!

The moon is a nocturnal place, the ultimate place for astronomy. Nowhere on earth do stars appear in such bewildering abundance as they do on the moon. The lunar sky is a spectacular field of stellar furnaces, brilliant light that has been traveling for hundreds, thousands, billions of years. The indescribable vastness of space is attainable here, where twice the light from each point reaches the moon as it does the earth. Colors of the cosmic dust, the distant spiraling galaxies, and the stars that compose them are seen as they never could be before. When a narrow beam from such a source is collected by a lunar telescope, its spectra can be recorded on film out to the very limit of their energy curves.

Classifying the stars by their ages and sizes as denoted by the colors they emit is a job that has been done only imperfectly and incompletely on earth. Undertaking this task on the moon, we might spend a year or ten years gathering a single spectrogram to analyze distant galaxies forever hidden from terrestrial lenses.

A lens on the moon weighs a sixth its earth weight, so that tubes or framework need be considerably less massive in the low gravity. Lenses and mirrors won't sag as much on the moon; we can build them as large as desired with minimum weight restrictions. There are no clouds, no wind vibrations, no fogging of the mirror, no perturbations of atmosphere, no convection distortions, no weather nor observatory domes to protect against it.

The combination of these conditions means we can build telescopes of a size never before considered possible. Optical behemoths to be employed in the optimal viewing environment of our sister planet will enable the observation of stars many times fainter than the dimmest star now visible from earth.

On the moon the practical powers of giant telescope

mirrors will begin to equal their theoretical powers of resolution. This means we can build mirrors and lenses much larger, increasing their magnifications many times over the instruments of earth, limited only by the resolutions of the lenses themselves. It should be noted that the magnification of a lens doesn't increase with size indefinitely, even on the airless moon, primarily because of chromatic aberration. This is the failure of a lens to produce exact point-to-point correspondence between an object and image due to the different ways each colored ray, or wavelength, of the spectrum is refracted, or bent. Achromatic mirrors on the moon, however, ought to be effective up to at least 2,000 inches, or ten times as big as the largest reflector telescope on earth.

Also on the moon astronomers at last can come to terms with their occupational hazard—the need to stay one step ahead of advancing industrialization. The growing city of Los Angeles, which already is encroaching on the Palomar telescope, and all other cities are 239,000 miles away. And the outpouring of terrestrial radio signals is shielded by the entire mass of the moon at our radio telescope site on the far side.

Anywhere on the moon we will see galaxies with increased contrast and can measure brightnesses of stars with magnitudes as low as 10,000. The "magnitude" of a star is its apparent brightness. The ancient Greeks devised the system, still in use, whereby the dimmest of stars ordinarily visible to the naked eye is +6, ranging upward to +1, 0, and −1 for very bright stars, −12 for the full moon as seen from earth, and −27 for the sun. Each successive step on the scale represents a 2.5 multiplication of brightness. When astronomers begin to work on the moon, no change will be required in the magnitude scale because the values already are corrected to outside atmosphere.

Most advantageous for a moon location, various

lunar instruments could be sensitive to the entire spectrum of electromagnetic radiation, from fractions of an angstrom to 10,000 kilometers in wavelength. (One angstrom, written simply "Å," is 10^{-10} meters or 4 billionths of an inch. Visible red light has a wavelength of about 6,500 Å and violet about 4,100 Å. Invisible infrared lightwaves are longer than 6,500 Å and invisible ultraviolet lightwaves are shorter than 4,100 A.)

In the face of this ability to measure the entire electromagnetic spectrum, it is difficult for astronomers to be negative toward the development of the moon. Indeed, the overwhelming majority (61.9%) of those who answered the astronomy questionnaire were in favor of a fast man-on-moon program. They felt NASA either should maintain its present pace or speed it up.

The 38.1% of astronomers who voted against the man-on-moon program offered the familiar money-could-be-spent-better criticism. But whereas geologists can say in truth that we know nothing of lunar materials, astronomers who oppose the project hardly can discount the advantages to astronomy. Instead, they created an alternative: put the telescope on an artificial satellite. That substitute suggestion was offered by virtually all the anti-moon base astronomers, and so it deserves examination.

Why go to the moon when we can orbit a telescope more easily?

It would be more economical to orbit an astronomical observatory than to go the greater distance to the moon. Such an artificial satellite would have the same advantages of airlessness as the lunar observatory. Optical and radio telescopes in space, as on the moon, would receive stellar light and radio signals before this radiation disperses in our atmosphere.

But such an orbiting observatory is only second best to one located on the moon. An astronomical satellite is a highly unstable platform, subject to the slightest planetary perturbations, hard to aim or keep on target, moving too fast to track a star for any useful length of time, and too close or in the midst of those great bands of radiation that guard the earth—radiation that eventually would distort photographic film, if not the image, and immediately would prevent men from working at the station for more than a few hours at a time.

On the other hand, if the observatory were unmanned, we would lose through television transmission most of the optical resolution we went into space to tain the giant dish antennas of radio telescopes. The remote control are formidable enough. Add to this the importance of visual observations, which would be lost, the impossibility of designing an instrument to cope with all unknowns, and the often critical need for immediate interpretations, and you begin to see why the station should be manned.

Advocates of satellite observatories recognize that there is no easy substitute for the astronomer at the eyepiece. So they suggest a large station in space, one that might be spun to simulate gravity, and sufficiently large to shield its occupants from the intense radiation of inner space!

It seems as though *not* going to the moon has become an objective in itself for all the schemes devised to build artificial moons to do these jobs imperfectly. I wonder whether a manned space station could be built sufficiently large to shield astronomers from the lethal Van Allen radiation. But even if it should, man's every physical action would cause an equal and opposite reaction on the orbiting station, hopelessly perturbing its orbit and making it useless for precise observations.

The station would have to be measured in miles, not only to solve the stability problem but also to contain the giant antennas of radio dish antennas. The new radar-radio bowl-shaped reflector set into the hills near Arecibo, Puerto Rico is 1,000 feet in diameter and has its electronic-feed platform suspended 500 feet above the bottom of the bowl. The feed system and associated focal point structure alone weigh 600 tons. We would want to build a radio reflector in space as large or even larger.

Optical telescopes have even more to gain from an extraterrestrial location — a prime reason for taking them to space, as has been explained, is so larger lenses can be used. But then the artificial satellite would grow bigger still. Also, housing the astronomers over great periods of time means the station would have to contain an enormous complex of machinery for life support, which would have to be serviced entirely by earth rocket. No doubt such a satellite could be put together in space. After all, it would require less power to launch the components of the station to an earth orbit than all the way to the moon.

But assembling a manned observatory in space and then maintaining and servicing it from earth would be a dead-end street. The satellite would have no opportunity in the years ahead of becoming self-sufficient through the utilization of materials such as will be found on the moon. No natural shelters would exist for personnel—an important consideration as we enter each period of sporadic sunspot activity. There would be no possibility of finding water for life and fuel. The artificial satellite would not obliterate the radio sounds of humanity, as would the entire mass of the moon. Nor could it change its orbit from equatorial to polar as easily as lunar telescopes could be constructed at various locations on the moon.

The moon is more than a goal for incurable romantics intrigued by the wonder of walking on another world (although that in itself seems laudable). It is an astronomical satellite already in orbit, awaiting only our tools and men to use them.

The gravity is weak enough to allow building radio and optical structures of the flimsiest construction, yet strong enough for men to work without disorientation.

It is close enough to the earth to allow profitable meteorological and geophysical observations, yet far enough away to avoid the earth's radiation belts.

It is large enough to provide stability, yet small enough to have no atmosphere to hinder observations.

Not only is the radiation environment more friendly, but micrometeoroids striking a given area of the moon are only a fraction of those that would strike the same area of a satellite near earth.

Further, telemetering information back to earth would be far simpler from a lunar observatory than from an orbiting station, whether either were manned or unmanned. Reason: the moon is visible from one point on earth for long enough at one time to complete a significant observing program and transmit the information without need for extensive data or command storage.

Despite these natural advantages of the moon over an orbiting space station, the decision over whether to build a large complex in space or to develop the moon bears heavily on our future goals. Defining these goals, in turn, depends in large measure on what raw materials we find on the moon. If the resources of the moon are anywhere near as plentiful as have been speculated, it would be senseless to trade them for a location in space. In the long run, it seems wiser to locate the observatory on the moon, for the moon is important not to any single purpose but to the sum of them all, from vacuum technology to mining to rocket launching for planetary exploration.

Given an observatory on the moon, what would we use it for? This question may be answered in four parts: seeing the moon from the moon, seeing the earth from the moon, seeing the solar system from the moon, and seeing the rest of the universe from the moon.

It may seem simpler to photograph the moon by walking around on its surface, as we do on earth, but there are reasons for supplementing this activity with one or more small telescopes.

The first men on the moon should photograph the distant landscape, as well as the closer surface features, to bring back as much data as possible. For instance, they can time the rising and setting of stars on the horizon to determine with precision the moon's rotation and revolution. (They are not *exactly* equal, resulting in a libration of the moon, such that we see in the course of time not half, but 59%, of the moon's surface from earth.)

They also may use the telescope to search for traces of lunar atmosphere, since a telescope on the surface of the moon is more than 200 times as sensitive as a telescope on earth with the same resolving power. To do this they would sight a star just off the horizon. At this angle, the starlight would traverse the maximum number of gas molecules in the "air" and its slightest perturbance could be measured. The resultant precise measurement of vacuum is important to future plans for research and manufacturing in the lunar vacuum. Further, by doing this sort of thing at various locations, searches can be made for areas of gaseous eruption— areas that would be of prime importance for finding usable materials.

Telescopes also could be used in conjunction with lasers to develop optical communication systems between two points on the moon's surface or between moon and earth. The term "laser" is an acronym for Light Amplification by Stimulated Emission of Radiation. The laser's most important characteristic is its ability to generate parallel beams of light (coherent radiation) at either infrared or visible frequencies. Its most promising use is in long-distance communications.

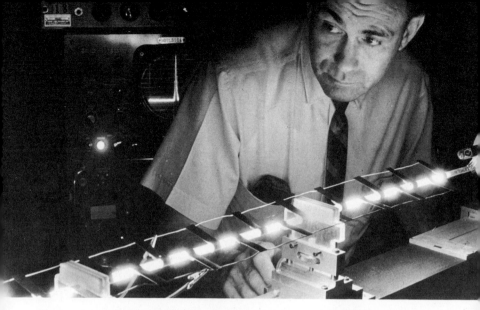

Lasers as communications devices may make more sense in space and on the moon where their signals can be modulated without atmospheric interference. Pulsed gas laser at Martin Co. is shown above. Below, a beam from a ruby laser is controlled by applying a magnetic field at Honeywell Research Center. The "smoke" is vapor from liquid nitrogen used to cool the apparatus.

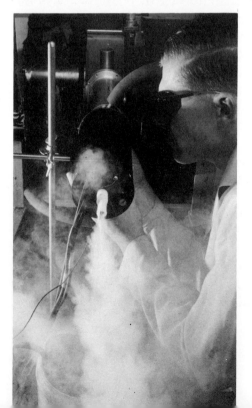

A recent report from the Air Force Cambridge Research Laboratories, Hanscom Field, Mass., maintains that coherent laser communication and detection systems probably will be feasible only in space. That is, we cannot expect to modulate a laser signal as we would a radio signal within the earth's atmosphere because clouds and atmospheric turbulences impress an undesirable modulation on the transmitted beam, garbling intelligence.

Actually, many of these experiments could be performed in advance of a manned landing. An 8-inch refractor and telemetering system to do such jobs has been designed by Northwestern University's Dearborn Observatory in a combined effort with The Hallicrafters Co. and Cook Electric Co., all in the Chicago area. In the proposed "Lunar Vacuum Observatory," the telescope is coupled with image sensors capable of sending a television frame back to earth every 17 minutes for an average of 85 pictures a day. The whole package weighs less than 100 earth pounds and is designed to last a year.

With men on the moon, telescopy becomes easier: the uncertainties of data transmission are replaced by on-the-spot intelligence and, more important, the telescope can be moved and pointed anywhere at will.

The next candidate for lunar observations is the earth itself. Even viewed by naked eye, the earth is an impressive place from a quarter of a million miles away. Distant enough to see in proper perspective, both mechanically and philosophically, it is sufficiently close to observe in all its variety and brilliance. At first it seems a great turquoise disc spotted with white, hanging in the sky some four times larger than we see the pale moon from earth. Then, between the streamers and puffs of gray and white cotton clouds, the blue of the Pacific shows and we are surprised momentarily to realize our earth is overwhelmingly a water planet.

Here and there, poking between the cotton like some sculptured abstraction are orange deserts, green fields, and white caps of ice at the poles. When the earth is "new," that is, when it is night on our planet, the lights of a metropolis twinkle forth, all but lost in the bright earthshine of a world considerably more reflectant than the moon. Surely the sight of earth alone must be numbered among reasons for going to the moon.

We will point our telescopes earthward for practical reasons though. That same view which will inspire poets of the 21st Century ought to render important contributions later in this century to the prediction of weather and even to its eventual modification.

The possibility of controlling a part of the weather at will certainly exists. Yet, in spite of meteorological balloons and satellites, airplanes that fly into hurricanes, cloud-seeding experiments, and an earthwide network of weather stations, we still do not know precisely and under exactly what conditions clouds form, rain falls, tornadoes are born, or lightning strikes. The major problem may be that all our vantage points are too close to the earth, and they are too fleeting. The weather satellites Tiros and Nimbus cannot return for a quick second look at a specific area, nor can they hover to study a storm in the making. Another disadvantage is that their pictures frequently lack landmarks when the cloud cover is extensive, often making identification impossible.

The surveys of various groups of scientists did not exclude meteorologists. These scientists voted overwhelmingly in favor of weather satellites over the moon as a base for weather observations of the earth. The questions were asked like this:

"Do you believe that an unmanned (instruments only) lunar base would advance the science of weather prediction significantly more than an unmanned orbiting space station?" More than 95% said "no."

"Do you believe that a manned lunar base would advance weather prediction or control significantly more than a manned orbiting space station?" Only 86.4% said "no" this time.

Now I have to admit that I agree with these views of most meteorologists (not necessarily because of their majority—after all, *all* meteorologists *could* be wrong). If we had to *choose* between a lunar weather base and a series of artificial weather satellites, the satellites would win hands down. Replacing weather satellites with a station on the moon is not part of the case for going to the moon. But using a lunar observatory *in conjunction with* weather satellites seems highly profitable and warrants the marriage of meteorology and astronomy.

Storm or hurricane tracks, cloud propagation, wind velocities, and front movements can be photographed at close intervals from a lunar observatory where half the earth can be seen at once. These large-scale pictures taken from the moon, during day or night, would show patterns that might escape the television cameras of widely spaced, close-orbiting satellites. In addition, pictures from the moon could assist the difficult task of fitting the Nimbus mosaics together.

It has been argued that we know now how hurricanes are formed. Yes we do. But we do not understand their vagaries: why they suddenly develop, collapse, or completely reverse their courses often in less than half a day—for no apparent reason. Watching a hurricane develop in its entirety over a long period of time and from a place as far away as the moon, where associated meteorological phenomena also can be observed over the whole earth (as it rotates), may contribute to our eventual breaking of these towering monsters of air.

Experiments now being tried attempt to go to the heart of the hurricane's heat engine: the great cumulonimbus clouds that form the wall of the eye. These clouds are seeded from the air with silver iodide crystals or dry ice in the hope that the balance of forces controlling the position of the clouds will be disrupted.

But it is guesswork at best—and dangerous guesswork. The first attempt at hurricane modification, in 1947, may have backfired. Two airplanes dumped 80 pounds of dry ice along a 110-mile inward track that ended just outside the eye wall of a moderately strong hurricane heading seaward about 400 miles off the Florida coast. Shortly after the seeding, the storm abruptly reversed its course and 43 hours later trampled over the state of Georgia causing considerable damage.

Whether the dry ice succeeded in changing the course of the hurricane is unknown because it was impossible to control the experiment or even to observe it in its totality. The incident is related here only to emphasize that a station on the distant and stable moon, always facing our terrestrial problems, would be ideal for coordinating the various phases of hurricane-control experiments.

Such a station also might prove useful in studying extraterrestrial influences on other weather phenomena, influences that meteorologists are beginning to think are more important than have been realized. Even now they are advocating more high-altitude rocket studies. They believe that natural cloud seeding occurs by the infall of micrometeoroids, that these plentiful cosmic particles provide the nuclei around which raindrops ultimately form.

If so, Dr. Fred L. Whipple, director of the Smithsonian Astrophysical Observatory at Harvard University, points out that the moon's gravity affects the concentration of space dust in the high atmosphere. Thus the moon affects our weather as the distance between it and the earth changes. Meteorologists long have known that the tides occurring in our oceans are repeated in the atmosphere, but didn't realize until recently that they help determine rainfall. While the effects are small compared to those of solar heating, these lunar forces may act as a trigger in setting off rain or snow.

Not only observations from the moon should be considered in enumerating merits of a lunar station. Observations at all altitudes from an increasing number of spacecraft a lunar base will engender also would contribute to a better understanding of how our weather is made.

Then too, a radio telescope on the moon, in conjunction with closer orbiting weather satellites, would help fathom the precise nature of the ionosphere. When the workings of these layers of heavily ionized molecules finally are detailed, it should become possible to predict their changes in advance and even to take some direct steps to control them, such as injecting silver iodide crystals by rocket.

Admittedly, the control of weather is speculation of the purest fashion, and it may be scores of years before any real steps are taken in this pursuit. But they will *never* be taken without completely detailed knowledge of the small and massive forces involved. Meanwhile, the road to modification is paved with other profitable successes; as we learn to predict storm routes more exactly, we can avoid their consequences.

While one lunar telescope is trained on the earth, others ought to be employed in the study of the rest of this system. For observing the "star of the solar system," the value of a lunar telescope becomes immediately evident. We may well be living in the atmosphere of the sun without being able to see it through our atmosphere which, it has been said with some poetic license, renders viewing the equivalent of observing the world from under about 35 feet of water.

Dinsmore Alter, director emeritus of the Griffith

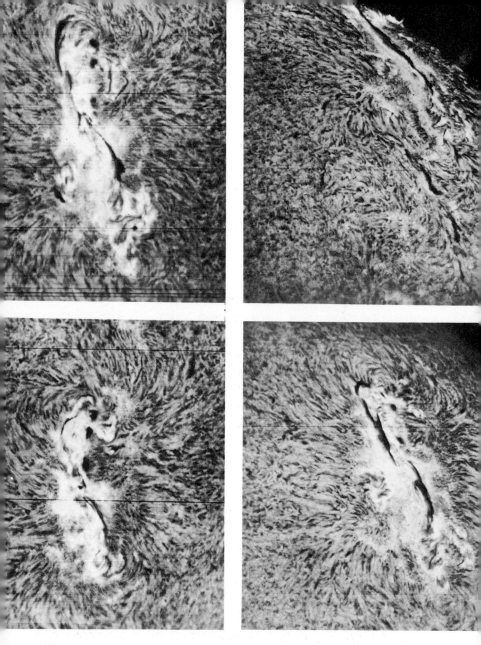

We never see the sunlight that causes storms due to the earth's heavy ocean of atmosphere, a problem that will be avoided when a meteorological station is located on the moon. Here, turbulent sections of the sun's chromosphere are photographed in red hydrogen light. Such sun storms are common.

Observatory, Los Angeles, wants to go to the moon, among other reasons, to follow coronal streamers out to the point where they probably envelop the earth. The ultimate key to all our weather, of course, is the sun. Yet, Alter points out, we never see the sunlight that causes storms.

"For many years," he explains, "I worked on solar relationships to our weather, and it always seemed that the light which comes to us with the least atmospheric interference is not the light which is most likely to affect our weather. Rather, it is the absorbed light which changes our atmosphere. This is something that we need to know about before we can hope to make long-range weather predictions. Although some of this information may be obtained from satellite observations, much more conclusive data can be obtained through observations from the moon."

In discussing solar observations, a few definitions are in order: The photosphere is the "surface" of the sun; that is, the luminous area beneath which we cannot see in the visible region of the spectrum. The chromosphere, above that, is several thousand miles thick and is composed mostly of hydrogen, which is responsible for the chromosphere's red color. The corona is the tenuous outermost part of the sun's atmosphere, extending for millions of miles from its surface.

The amount of ultraviolet light emitted from the photosphere is relatively small compared to that of the hotter chromosphere and corona. Thus, the behavior of the chromosphere and corona is studied best by observing the ultraviolet emission from the sun, particularly in the wavelengths around 300 angstroms—precisely the region most completely blacked out by our atmosphere. In the 3,000-year-old history of astronomy, mankind's first look at the sun in the ultraviolet and x-ray regions had to wait until March 7, 1962, the day the first Orbiting Solar Observatory was launched.

Mankind's first look at the sun in the ultraviolet and x-ray regions took place on March 7, 1962 when the first Orbiting Solar Observatory was launched. This one — OSO II — was orbited Feb. 3, 1965 for additional solar measurements. It carries ten sample reflective coatings (at arrow), which absorb ultraviolet light differently, telling spacemen which one to use to protect Apollo on its seven-day manned flight to the moon. The two black circles absorb nearly all the solar radiation, thus determining the total quantity received by the satellite.

That satellite did not carry a telescope, but was equipped to monitor solar emissions of several different wavelengths over a period of months. During this time the sun was both quiet and violent. The measurements proved that nonthermal processes are present and important in the corona at *all* times, including periods of tranquility.

Even these comparatively minor findings are of great value to astronomers and meteorologists in piecing together the complexities of our weather. But they are as nothing compared to the continuous observations of the sun that could be made from a manned optical and radio observatory on the moon.

From the moon, aurorae in the northern and southern hemispheres of earth could be studied simultaneously during solar outbursts. Then too, we could observe star occultations behind the earth's atmosphere with precision, according to Dr. J. Allen Hynek, director of Northwestern's astronomy department. Dr. Hynek is author of the proposal for the instrumented lunar observatory described earlier. He also heads a group that recently proposed to NASA a plan for the manned placing of an unmanned 12-inch telescope on the moon. Hynek suggests that:

"Photometric observations of stellar extinction would give information about scattering and absorption in the upper air, and it may be that refraction measures will yield density information at high altitudes above the earth. The ability to examine the entire periphery of the earth [from the moon] will permit a view of large-scale phenomena—for example, differences in airglow over continents as opposed to oceans."

Similarly, observing the planets from the moon will be enormously simplified. It is difficult enough to be limited to that part of the spectrum not absorbed by the molecules of our atmosphere. But when the object you view from the bottom of our air is a planet with an atmosphere of its own, the unscrambling of atmospheres is perplexity compounded. No wonder then that Venus, perpetually shrouded in dense clouds, remains a mystery. We know next to nothing about the surface of the planet closest to earth, despite optical and radio telescopy, despite radar measurements — and even despite the Mariner II flyby launched on Aug. 27, 1962. This Mariner came as close as 20,900 miles on Dec. 14 in that year and measured the temperature across the Venusian disc in both the infrared and microwave regions. The results seemed to confirm the supposition that earlier high radio measurement of Venus' temperature—a flaming 800 F—are not merely the result of microwave emission from its ionosphere, but actually represent the temperature of its surface.

Dr. John Strong, director of the Johns Hopkins Astrophysics Laboratory, strongly disagrees. He feels that the radio emission detected could have arisen from massive lightning storms in the turbulent, dense clouds. The actual surface might not be a torrid desert after all. Temperatures might be similar to those on earth, and life as we know it might exist!

Unwilling to wait until a permanent observatory could be established on the moon where Venus and other objects could be measured over infinitely long periods of time, Strong directed an unmanned balloon flight in October, 1964. The balloon provided about three hours of instrumented observation at 86,000 feet, above most of the earth's atmosphere. During this time a spectrometer measured Venusian clouds in the infrared.

The results are in flat disagreement with those of Mariner II and terrestrial radio measurements. The Venusian clouds were shown to be composed of ice particles and the upper atmosphere to be about as humid as that of the earth. Thus the atmosphere is not formed of dust or noxious chemicals as had been theorized, and the surface temperature may be much lower than Mariner indicated.

The exciting question of whether life could exist on Venus will be explored in the next chapter. But information about Venus—a planet that is so similar to the earth's size, weight, mass, and distance from the sun that it is virtually a double—is important in other ways too.

The mystery of Venus enters basic physical research in the most fundamental of questions: the origin of the solar system and the universe itself. Radar observations from the earth's largest antenna in Puerto Rico confirm those obtained recently by Caltech's Jet Propulsion Laboratory. They say that Venus is spinning slowly backwards—a state of affairs contrary to the counter-clockwise traffic pattern of the otherwise uniform solar system and one that could upset the widely held view that the sun and planets were formed from a spinning cloud of gas and dust. For if the planets were born of such a nebula, all of them would inherit its spin. They would rotate on their axes as well as revolve around the sun in the same direction.

When, early in the century, several satellites of the outer planets were found to orbit backwards, it was merely necessary to assume that these wrongway little moons were simply captured asteroids. The detection of the first of these, a satellite of Saturn called Phoebe, gave rise to the verse:

> Never mind what God has said,
> We have made a law instead.
> So, small moon, you'd better change;
> Really, we can't rearrange
> All our charts from Mars to Hebe
> Just to fit a chit like Phoebe.

But Venus isn't a chit like Phoebe, and if it truly

rotates in a direction opposite that of all the other planets, as now seems conclusive, astronomers may have to revise one of their most widely cherished theories.

Struggling to preserve the dust-cloud theory, Cornell University's Dr. Thomas Gold suggests that Venus once was locked toward the sun, as is Mercury, a common occurrence for bodies close to their primaries. But whereas Mercury has no atmosphere, Venus has an extremely dense one. Perhaps the violent circulation of this atmosphere resulting from the heating of only the sunward side led to an asymmetrical bulge of the atmosphere toward the sun, postulates Gold. The gravitational forces of the sun, pulling on this bulge, then caused Venus to spin slowly backwards.

The discovery of this retrograde rotation in 1964 followed the development and widespread application of radar some years before. In astronomy, as in all the sciences, discoveries await the inventions of technology. Had Leonardo been in possession of a reciprocating engine, he might have constructed a helicopter. And when Johann Kepler, who believed in orderliness, reasoned in 1610 that Mars ought to have two satellites, astronomers searched for these moons for centuries. They found them only in 1877, shortly after the 26-inch refractor at Washington was built, the world's largest telescope at that time. Once found, the satellites were put to immediate use in calculating the mass of Mars with a high degree of accuracy. The example is repeated everywhere in the history of science. Nature is a jigsaw puzzle, the solution of which is made possible by technology, which is made possible by science . . .

The greatest technological breakthrough of several centuries will be an observatory on the moon. It is an accomplishment as far-reaching as the invention of the telescope itself, for it will carry our state of knowledge at least as far as the early telescopes took science from naked-eye observations. A base on the moon will permit new light to be shed on our lenses, light of a fuller spectrum, light that has never been seen before. A radio telescope there will do even more.

It is remarkable in this age of nuclear power, rockets, and plans to land men on the moon by 1970 to realize that it was not until 1931 that radio waves of extraterrestrial origin were discovered. Few people even suspected their existence before then! And it was not until 1955 that planetary radio astronomy began.

Jupiter was the first planet noticed to be emitting strong outbursts. Since then, thermal radio signals have been obtained from five planets, but Jupiter still appears to be alone among the planets in radiating powerful *nonthermal* radio noise.

Indications are strong that both the intensity and frequency of occurrence of Jovian radiations are greater below five megacycles than the band above that where ground-based observations now are limited. These low-frequency observations are screened completely by the earth's ionosphere.

The greatest number of radio studies of Jupiter have been made by University of Florida astronomers. Dr. Alex G. Smith, professor of physics and astronomy there, believes it is important to get above our atmosphere to observe the stronger Jovian radio signals because a correlation may exist between the Jovian outbursts and solar and geophysical events. Even more important, he thinks a radio telescope in space or on the moon pointed at Jupiter would break the secret of how radio noise is generated. Such knowledge then could be applied to stellar astronomy.

Despite the existence in our system of nine planets, 31 natural satellites, about 30,000 asteroids, some 100-billion comets, and countless specks of dust, stray molecules, and dissociated atoms, 99.86% of all the

Radio telescopes on the moon might be constructed economically like this one at Ohio State University. The array consists of two 100-foot antennas separated by 3½ acres of aluminum-covered concrete. On the weatherless moon, aluminum-coated plastic sheet would suffice for the ground reflector.

Natural radio signals coming from celestial objects are scooped up by this steerable ten-story high dish antenna of the University of Michigan radio telescope. The advantages of radio telescopes on the moon would be to focus specific radio signals of very short wavelength and, especially, of very long ones — signals now blocked by the earth's atmosphere and ionosphere.

matter in this solar system resides in the sun. Yet the sun is an absurdly small sample of the universe. The famous Dr. Harlow Shapley, director emeritus of the Harvard Observatory, has estimated from various sample counts that there are 200-billion stars in our galaxy alone, and more than 100-quintillion stars in the total observable universe!

No wonder, then, that the stars, galaxies, and cosmic smoke and gas are the major subjects of astronomy. In our anthropocentric concern with the terrestrial problems, the Cosmos is usually forgotten, and men always ask, "What good do astronomers do for the world?" When asked that question, Shapley always answers, "What do you mean by world?"

The case for an observatory on the moon is a case for seeing the universe more clearly. It is only that, and it is all of that. When almost all astronomers in the U.S. were asked, by mail questionnaire, what they consider to be the most important scientific questions facing astronomy today, they answered almost universally: the organization of the universe—including the origin, structure, formation, and evolution of stars and planets.

Why go to the expense of placing a telescope on the moon when more than a billion galaxies, each with countless stars, are within our present reach? We are limited now not only by our atmosphere but by cosmic smoke that absorbs the starlight from beyond and makes it difficult to see farther than a few billion light-years. The answer is simply that we will see more of the seeable and hear more of the hearable. These inputs will drive us deeper into the deepest of all inquiries concerning the evolution of the atoms of which all matter is composed and the creation, evolution, and destiny of the total universe.

The scientific probe into creation in this seventh decade of the 20th Century is enveloped in two inadequate theories, both stained by religion and the scientific upbringing of the cosmologist, both interpreting data limited by the almost opaque windows in our air. The first postulates an all-inclusive Primeval Atom, which broke apart some 10-billion years ago, beginning time and space, and expanding forever thereafter. The theory accounts for the observed scattering of the galaxies and the creation of all the atoms out of quanta of energy or out of the protons, electrons, neutrons, and mesons of atoms.

The second sidesteps the problem of creation by denying there ever was a creation. The universe had no beginning and no end. It is in a "steady state," evolution is merely local, and the universe as a whole does not progress or regress continuously.

Evidence from the earth's largest optical telescope supports only a modification of this theory: alternate expansions and contractions seem to vary proportionately with distance, suggesting a "pulsating" universe. Thus, the expansion velocity at a million lightyears is thought to be 20 miles a second, at 100-million lightyears 2,000 miles a second, and at a billion lightyears 20,000. Whether this expansion of space is a mere "local" phenomenon on the cosmic clock may be unanswerable, but it is ours always to reason why.

Are space and time infinite? It is hard to imagine walls around the galaxies with or without space on the other side, much less inanimate evolution ever ceasing at some point in time. Telescopes are time machines, penetrating the past by the number of lightyears a star is distant. We know the earth is 4.5-billion years old and reason the sun formed perhaps a billion years before that. But since we cannot see stars anywhere near as far as 4- or 5-billion lightyears, we have no direct evidence that the universe always existed or even that it is any older than our own tiny planet.

Why is the sky dark between the stars? After all, if the universe is infinite, then in whatever direction we look, provided we could peer deeply enough into space, eventually we should see stars. In 1912, V. M. Slipher, of Lowell Observatory, Flagstaff, Ariz., discovered that the spectral lines of a given galaxy were displaced slightly and they occurred on a slightly longer wavelength than expected; that is, they were displaced toward the red end of the spectrum.

This widely known "red shift" has been explained most easily by light being emitted from a moving source, just as a train whistle decreases in pitch as it speeds away. The light that falls on our telescopes from a distant galaxy will have shifted so greatly that it appears mostly in the infrared. To be visible by the time it reaches us, the light would have started out at the other end of the spectrum—in the ultraviolet where very little energy is emitted. Thus the light from galaxies beyond a certain distance is small and our observation of the universe is self-limited.

It will be interesting to learn what the view from the moon will reveal about the state of the universe, since without an obscuring atmosphere, we will be able to "see" into those infrared windows now closed to terrestrial lenses.

Such a view of the universe from the moon may help bring order out of the hopefully-temporary chaos the remarkable discovery of "quasi-stellar sources" has conjured in recent years. These "quasars" and newly discovered "interlopers" may have as great an impact on physical thought as the discovery that the stars do not revolve around the earth!

That statement is not exaggerated. The 50 or so quasars so far discovered appear to be entirely new kinds of astronomical "objects." Lying at the limit of earthly observation, their red shifts are so great that they have been measured to be speeding away from us at 76,000 miles per second, or about half the speed of light. Since speed of recession is proportionate to distance, the quasars are at least 4-billion lightyears away, the most distant objects yet identified.

To be visible at such a vast distance, it has been calculated that a luminous source must give as much light as ten of the brightest galaxies each containing some 100-billion stars. Even more inconceivable is the fact that quasars have been observed to vary in brilliance as much as 10% *a month!* Now, since nothing can travel faster than light—the cornerstone of the physics we know—any object that changes in brilliance hardly can be larger than the distance such light would travel during the period of fluctuation. Thus, quasars flickering as fast as they do must be less than one lightyear in diameter—a fantastic deduction when you think about it, for it means that the energy of a trillion stars is contained in a volume too small to hold them!

In other words, at the state of our present confusion, quasars are impossible! Either the observations are wrong, or quasars follow physical laws entirely unknown.

If large radio and optical telescopes were not available, quasars would not have been discovered. If bigger ones are built, and placed in an environment such as the moon affords, where their increased size will contribute to greater resolving power, then the riddle of quasars may begin to have meaning. In the face of such incredible energy as quasars seem to possess—and incredible knowledge that unlocking their secrets promises—objections to an observatory on the moon, or any other major step toward understanding, lose all potency.

Of similarly hard-to-answer proportions is the question concerning the origination of the stars and planets. The dust-cloud hypothesis described in Chapter IV is, without a doubt, the most widely held by cosmologists and ordinary astronomers alike.

Yet, the highly respected Prof. A. Dauvillier, of Pic-du-Midi Observatory in France, who has studied the origins and significance of cosmic dust for 30 years, claims that the accretion of dust into stars or planets is nonsense. Cosmic dust possesses a kinetic energy such that collisions would cause it to evaporate. It carries a positive charge through a photoelectric effect so that electrostatic repulsion between the particles is incomparably greater than their gravitational attraction. Thus, clouds do not conglomerate, but on the contrary they disperse or are captured by low-temperature stars.

Where did stars come from? They were always there, says Dauvillier. And they might as well have been since we are no closer to the "fundamental" truth if we prove that the stars were formed of dust than if we prove that the dust was formed of stars.

"There is nothing to justify the supposition that the universe has ever presented an appearance different from that which it offers today. Further, nothing is less primitive than cosmic dust, which requires a lengthy preliminary evolution through atoms, molecules, crystalline minerals, and celestial bodies. Cosmic dust represents a final—assuming there to be one —rather than an initial state. The rings of asteroids and those of Saturn are much more the debris of a terrestrial planet than of embryonic celestial bodies."

To account for the creation of planets and satellites, Dauvillier postulates a theory of "twin stars" and "twin planets." Double stars are extremely abundant. They originate frequently through pseudoshocks entailing tidal effects. When these effects become substantial, the energy loss leads to capture. More rarely, central collisions occur. These are catastrophic events accompanied by nuclear reactions whereby hyperdense stars engender new massive giant red stars of great volume formed from new elements.

Somewhat more frequently than central collisions, but still much more rarely than pseudoshocks, grazing collisions of stars cause stellar capture followed by a series of tangential grazing collisions. This is what happened to our sun: two stars fused into a single whole, resulting in an unstable and ephemeral system that produced planets.

Just as two stars are needed to engender a planetary system, two planets are needed to engender a system of satellites. Just as there exist at least two classes of stars, the giants and dwarfs, there also are two families of planets, large and small, and two families of satellites—as is shown by Titan or Iapetus (the largest of Saturn's nine satellites) on the one hand, and the majority of satellites on the other.

Absolute symmetry does not exist in nature. The masses of the two proto-stars are not exactly the same, nor are the twin planets identical. The greater their asymmetry, the fewer revolutions they need accomplish before interacting. The length of time they exist as double planets conditions their ultimate fate, and so Dauvillier hypothesizes events of three types:

■ *The Saturn type,* where double proto-Saturns grazed while still gaseous, giving rise to a satellite system consisting of the giants Titan and Iapetus, and the dwarfs—just as the double Sols fused to form the giant and dwarf planets. Twin Jupiters and twin Uranuses, however, fused without prior capture, and so engendered through oscillation only one family of dwarfs each, thus explaining the different surface rotation speeds of the sun and the giant planets.

■ *The terrestrial type,* where each twin of Mercury, Venus, and Mars fused at the end of several centuries in molten state, and so could not engender satellites. (Dauvillier wrote me saying that the retrograde rotation of Venus, discussed earlier as upsetting the dust-cloud theory of planet formation, can be interpreted *only* by the theory of twin planets.)

In the exceptional case of the earth, the twins fused

tangentially, thereby imparting a considerable angular momentum that led to the earth-moon system, a true double planet. Thus, the moon should have evolved as did the earth, complete with a hot, though smaller, interior; volcanism; usable compounds closer to the surface than the earth, because it is smaller and cooled faster; and all the other materials speculated in Chapter IV.

■ *"Olbers' planets,"* orbiting between Mars and Jupiter, which were so small they captured each other in the solid state at the end of their chemical and mineralogical evolution. They collided after solidification, broke up, and formed the asteroids. Just as the twin Olbers' planets were the smallest of the solar system, the twin satellites that gave birth to the rings of Saturn were the smallest satellites in the system.

It took a long time for the twins of Olbers' planet to interact, and even longer for the accumulation of perturbations of Jupiter on these small bodies to scatter them to form the rings of asteroids. It took longer still for some to be expelled as far as Uranus and Mars. Thus Dauvillier accounts for the tiny moons of Mars and why the innermost, Phobos, only 3,500 miles away from its primary and within the critical limit of instability, was captured too recently to have fallen.

How can Dauvillier's theory, or any of the many others too numerous to outline in a book of this scope, be proved or disproved?

Accumulation of evidence, pro or con, is the only deserving answer to that question, for no theory is necessarily correct, by definition. Here, a lunar observatory will help, since it will extend our senses significantly. A comparison may be made with the initial discoveries of radio astronomy. Twenty years ago, the space separating the galaxies was thought to be a complete void. The existence of a "bridge" of luminous matter between our galaxy and the Great Magellanic

Cloud then was verified by radio measurements.

Now *many* intergalactic clouds and bridges are thought to exist, arising from tidal effects operating between neighboring galaxies and stretching over thousands or millions of lightyears! Out in the black space between galaxies, where the mean free path of an atom may be 100-million miles and lasts a year or more, few of these bridges of hydrogen atoms and molecules can be detected from earth. But their existence may be confirmed, and defined, by observations from the moon in those wavelengths now screened by our atmosphere.

Just as an understanding of extraterrestrial matter is necessary to extend our knowledge of physics and chemistry, the detection of extraterrestrial life will begin a new science of comparative biology, and will bridge the gap between inanimate and animate evolution. One of the most compelling reasons for the study of astronomy—and potentially the most important—is the search for extraterrestrial intelligent life. If, as Dauvillier believes, stars form planets only by the comparatively rare grazing collisions of stars, then our chances of communicating with intelligence elsewhere will be restricted.

On the other hand, there are a lot of stars. Shapley points out that of the more than 100-quintillion stars, fully 20% are essentially identical with Sol in luminosity, chemistry, and size. These ought to have planets, and some of these planets ought to have life, and some of that life ought to have evolved intelligence, as possibly has ours.

Chapter **7**

WITNESS:

WHEREAS, the moon offers a relatively nearby, low gravity, and airless place for launching spacecraft to the planets, as well as for observations of planets and stars; and

WHEREAS, the potentially most important reason for going to space is to break through to knowledge of comparative biology and knowledge of all science many orders of magnitude greater than possible by staying at home; and

WHEREAS, the far side of the moon is a quiet radio telescope site for communicating with intelligences elsewhere, should they exist;

NOW, THEREFORE, the most extensive of all arguments for going to the moon will be advanced: to find, compare, and perhaps even communicate with extraterrestrial life.

(TIME ESTIMATE for contacting intelligent extraterrestrial life: 2000+.)

the case for
life beyond earth

THE MOST EXCITING of the cases for going to the moon surely must be the case for finding extraterrestrial life.

In the low gravity and lack of atmospheric friction we can send our spaceships from the moon with much greater efficiency and economy than from earth. Without hindrance of atmosphere we can train our telescopes on those stars suspected of having planets. In the absence of air and probably of magnetic fields or ionosphere, where the windows to the full electromagnetic spectrum are wide open all of the time—and on the far side where the radio noise from earth is blocked —we can listen for the sounds of intelligence.

Beyond minimal efforts already begun on earth, therefore, the search for extraterrestrial life, from microbes to men to supermen, logically begins on the moon.

During the last two decades, thousands of measurements of the peculiar orbits of seven stars reported in the cramped "literature" of astronomy went all but unnoticed by most scientists and almost all laymen. Yet

the conclusions finally drawn from these observations
in the last few years have been so startling that, had
laymen on this planet either the desire or the astronomers' sanction to find out about them, headlines like
the following would have been published in every
newspaper in the world:

EXISTENCE OF PLANETS OUTSIDE
SOLAR SYSTEM CONFIRMED

During this period, other unpublicized experiments
changed, or should have changed, the thought processes
of the scientists, philosophers, and theologians. For in
those years, at the University of California, University of Chicago, Florida State University, and elsewhere, objects that came very close to what biologists
think of as "living things" were made in the laboratory
from inanimate matter. The headline in this case might
have shouted, perhaps more correctly than not:

'LIFE' CREATED IN LABORATORY

Now I am fully aware that most scientists with
knowledge of the two sets of observations referred to
will hold these cases to be a sensational beginning to
an inherently sensational subject. Most of them will
become immediately defensive and insist that "Sensational headlines like yours are exactly what we try to
avoid to guard the integrity and precision of science."

I believe that science *is* sensational today, that
science should be everybody's business, and that it
ought to become at least as popular as night baseball—
while still remaining honest and precise. The opposite
course is for science to remain isolated from everyday
life, for man to remain apart from the rest of the universe with which he is evolving. Too many scientists
do their best to form an exclusive hierarchy. Too
many peer with cold indifference on all attempts by
non-scientists to speculate on scientific matters—a

ridiculous attitude since most scientists are laymen in any branch of science other than their own.

These observations do not excuse scientific ignorance among the general populace. Rather, this ignorance is a cause of scientists' isolation. Laymen for the most part would rather plug themselves into the living room cathode ray tube than let anything so intellectually "difficult" as science intrude upon them. Lacking motivation to learn, they instinctively fear the power and the impersonality of science. Perhaps because their minds are atrophied, whereas those of the scientists are merely busy forming a priesthood, laymen can be forgiven.

Into this medley of H. G. Wellsian Morlocks and Eloi has blown a refreshing breeze of entertainment-literature called science fiction, which has as its main theme the existence of other worlds and other intelligences. I approach the case for life beyond earth via science fiction for two reasons: the dramatic stimulus offered by good and poor science fiction has torn at least a million laymen away from cowboy stories, making them amenable to therapy. And because, like it or not, scientists and engineers today are performing actual research into the tenets of science fiction. "Life" today may mean more than terrestrial life.

I do not suggest that scientists should learn from science fiction (this would be to reverse the logical and established flow), or even that they necessarily should be stimulated by it. I do claim that scientists and engineers — especially those doing R&D — should resist phlegmatic tendencies to rest on "leading scientific authority*," that the powerful scientific elite should take care not to behave dogmatically, as the powerful church did in Galileo's time; that researchers should foster the spirit of adventurous thinking and skepti-

---

*It was a leading scientific authority, Dr. Simon Newcomb, who proved that heavier-than-air machines could never fly.

cism over today's assumed truths. In Faraday's words, we should "suspend judgment until our ideas and hypotheses become laws."

We have in the history of mankind no greater opportunity to revitalize adventurous scientific thought than we do today in these early moments of space travel. Yet a strong attitude is prevalent among scientists that any article or book proposing the possibilities of something fantastic is somehow *less scientific* than the opposite, familiar view — *even when the scientific evidence pro or con is nonexistent!*

The arguments to follow take the fantastic view not because it is *per se* any more accurate than the orthodox, but because it is more fruitful. It can point to directions for future scientific inquiry. The conservative approach should not be allowed to dominate science, for it can lead easily to intolerance and stagnation. The sooner scientists admit that trips to the moon, exobiology, and radio telescopes aimed to receive broadcasts from intelligent beings on other planetary systems *are* sensational, and become excited over the sensation, the sooner they can achieve breakthroughs in this area.

The two isolated and sensational, though underpublicized, series of events given newspaper status above lead to this prediction: ultimately the most important consequence of the utilization of the moon — as the first major step in the development of space — will be the proof or denial that life, and possibly intelligent life, exists elsewhere in the universe.

The first step in the search is to assess the likelihood of planets where life could be. The chances seem nil in our solar system for life beyond earth, Mars, and possibly Venus, which will be discussed later. The other billions of stars may have planets, but no one has ever seen one.

No one has ever seen an electron or an atom, either.

That planets exist outside our solar system is inferred — in a way not too dissimilar to inferences made about the existence of electrons, whose effects are noted in electron microscopes or television sets.

A star and its planet, planets, or nonluminous dwarf-star companions revolve around a common center of gravity, just as earth and moon revolve each month around a point that lies some 1,000 miles beneath the earth's surface. These gravitational effects perturb the motions of some stars so that their transverse movements are not linear but are unevenly sinusoidal. That is, the paths of some stars over a period of years are not straight lines, but wavy ones.

One example: between 1916 and the present, 50 astronomers participated in the photographing of more than 2,400 plates with over 8,000 exposures of the second closest known stellar body called "Barnard's Star," some six lightyears distant. (The nearest, at 4.3 lightyears, is the triple star system Alpha Centauri.) After these many measurements, the astronomers finally agreed conclusively that Barnard's Star was being perturbed by a planet. That planet was calculated to have a mass of 0.0015 of our sun, or about 60% greater than Jupiter's.

Dr. Peter Van de Kamp, of Sproul Observatory, Swarthmore College, Swarthmore, Pa., in describing these conclusions of a quarter-century's observations, wrote:

"An inspection of the best plates reveals no sign of any companion, as indeed is to be expected because of the small mass, indicated by the small amplitude of the perturbation. Were a companion seen in the predicted positional angle, its very visibility would imply a mass sufficiently large to cause a much larger perturbation than is observed. In other words, somewhat paradoxically, a visible companion would disprove the very prediction which would have led to its discovery.

... We shall interpret this result as a companion of Barnard's Star, which therefore appears to be a planet: that is, an object of such a low mass that it would not create energy by the conventional nuclear conversion of hydrogen into helium."

Barnard's planet, according to Van de Kamp, would appear to us as an object fainter than the 30th visual magnitude, beyond the reach of existing instruments on earth — but not beyond significantly larger instruments that could be assembled on the moon where distortion and other size limitations are virtually absent.

There is today reasonably good evidence for the existence of invisible planetary companions of seven stars — all of them being among the 100 nearest to earth. These are:

STAR	YEAR PLANETARY PERTURBATION ASSERTED	APPROX. MASS OF MAJOR PLANET (in solar units)	DISTANCE FROM EARTH (in lightyears)
Barnard's Star	1963	0.0015	6.0
Lalande 21185	1960	0.03	8.2
61 Cygni (double star)	1942	0.016	11.1
Krueger 60A (double star)	1953	0.009+	12.7
Bd + 20° 2465	1943	0.03	15.5
Ci 2354	1958	0.02	17.7
η Cas*	1948	0.01	18.0

COMPARISON			
Earth	—	0.000003003	—

Existence not completely established.

If seven stars have been seen to have perturbed paths, why not 700, or 7,000?

As the table above shows, only large planets, more

massive than Jupiter, have been detected. Perhaps smaller planets exist, but they do not perturb their stars sufficiently to be noticed. And almost all stars are so far away that their apparent motions are extremely small and very difficult to measure. The seven stars listed are close enough to the earth for repeated precise measurements. Says astronomer Harlow Shapley: "Some unseen celestial neighbor must be causing that wavelike deviation of 61 Cygni from straight-line motion."

From sampling the contents of space with the largest telescopes to distances in excess of a billion light-years, Shapley estimates that there are more than 100-billion galaxies and a total star population in excess of 10^{20} (1 followed by 20 zeros). He and other astronomers take a guess at this point. They reason that "if only one star in 100 were single like our sun, there still would be a tremendous number of single stars—more than 10^{18}. And if only one in 100 has a system of planets, and only one in 100 of these has an earth-type planet, and only one in 100 earth-type planets is of the proper distance from its sun-type star, and of them only one in 100 has a chemistry of air, water, and land something like ours ..."

The conclusion, if you're interested in mental gymnastics, comes out to 10-billion planets suitable for life like ours. The conclusion, however, is "unproved." We have little more reason to estimate one in 100 than we have to estimate one in 10^{20}, which would leave us, unfortunately, with earth alone.

But the case for finding extraterrestrial life has just begun! In a volume of 10,000 cubic parsecs (a parsec is 3.26 lightyears, or 19-trillion miles), there are about 1,000 visible main-sequence stars.

Why aren't there more?

Dr. Shiv S. Kumar, NASA Goddard Space Flight Center, and Dr. Harrison Brown, director of geological sciences at Caltech, bring the mathematician's viewpoint to bear on the problem. Studying distribution of these stars by luminosity, Kumar has shown their frequency to increase rapidly until about 13 magnitudes, after which they suddenly and mysteriously fall off. It is not reasonable to assume that this decrease of observed frequency with increasing magnitude represents an actual drop in the frequency of bodies. It just doesn't seem realistic that stars of the 14th magnitude should be dramatically less plentiful than stars of the 13th. Yet the curve of distribution (see chart on next page) shows stars of the 19th magnitude to be only a tenth as plentiful as those of the 12th!

The answer cannot be found entirely in the fact that as stars become fainter they become increasingly difficult to see. Our telescopes certainly are capable of resolving 13th magnitude stars.

A more reasonable answer may be found in Kumar's calculations that bodies smaller than about 0.07 the mass of the sun cannot support thermonuclear reactions and are therefore invisible. These cold bodies, or "black dwarfs," probably are more numerous than luminous bodies.

Correcting the distribution curves of stars, Brown suggests that frequencies of bodies in space follow the straight line shown. Extrapolating from this line he estimates that there are about 60 unseen bodies larger than Mars (and many smaller) for every visible star. Further, he estimates that 4.2% of black dwarfs would receive a heat flux equivalent to that received in our solar system from Venus through the asteroid belt, an area where most exobiologists believe life processes can take place. Thus, such calculations indicate that more than two planets per visible star might provide suitable environments for the emergence of life — life, that is, based on earth-like heat requirements.

Again, this and similar lines of statistical specula-

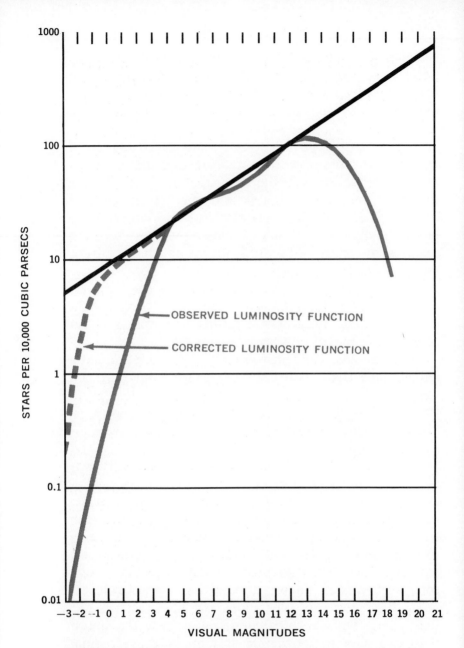

Quantity of bodies in space more likely follows straight line shown, rather than the "observed luminosity" curve revealed by telescopes. Additional bodies are non-luminous stars and planets.

tion are not proof positive. But the circumstantial evidence grows stronger now, and the value of the speculation becomes evident. For if astronomers are as convinced that most stars have planets, as biologists, for instance, are that viruses are a cause of cancer, the directions for further research are obvious. Just as we examine all viruses in every conceivable aspect to determine their role in the formation of tumors, we should examine all stars for offspring.

If planetary systems are abundant, life also *can* be abundant. Its pursuit not only would be exciting, but profitable in several ways: it would lead to an understanding of life; an extended theory of evolution, ranging from the formation of stars to the formation of intelligence (or other "goal"); and the learning from alien intellects vastly superior to *homo sapiens*. Let's explore these three possibilities.

The understanding of life has progressed with startling rapidity. When, a half-century ago, artificial parthenogenesis — the power to replace the sperm cell in animals by chemical agents of different kinds — was discovered, scientists couldn't believe their own eyes; it meant, among other things, that these creatures carry a double charge of heredity from the mother's side. Even human spermatozoa now can be frozen in contact with diluted glycerine for long periods without losing their power to fertilize. Artificial mutations can be produced by means of penetrative radiations or of certain poisons such as mustard gas, thereby causing new races of living creatures to appear on earth. Add to this all of the contributions of biology in combating disease, healing injuries, grafting organs, etc., and it is clear that we now have the means of acting upon life.

Yet, for all these and many more exclamatory discoveries of biology, the understanding of life hardly has begun. We cannot create life — at least, not yet. As the inventor of parthenogenesis has said in utter humility, "we only plagiarize nature." Biology does not prolong life; its conquests merely have halted some killers of life. It does not determine sex. It does not control heredity to increase intelligence, to prevent feeble-mindedness, or to do anything else. It does not tell us how to save a tenth of our population from their serious neuroses and psychoses. It does not save us from the fatality of many diseases or accidents, nor even from the discomforts of minor afflictions. Yet all of these and other problems, the practical and the profound, are being battered by biology and would succumb to some deeper understanding of life: an understanding awaiting us, perhaps, on other planets or other solar systems.

Many biochemists believe that life is not only possible elsewhere, but inevitable if the right temperature, chemical, and other conditions come into balance. In 1951, Dr. Melvin Calvin and his associates at the University of California, Berkeley, attempted to create the conditions for life to emerge from inanimate matter. This and other recent work give substance to the "inevitability" hypothesis of life on other earth-type planets.

Calvin bombarded aqueous solutions of inorganic materials with high-energy ionizing radiation, using the 60-inch cyclotron at the university. The idea here was to answer the question that if life originated in an organic milieu, as is commonly believed, how did the organic milieu originate from inorganic materials?

Calvin's experimental results showed that high-energy radiation, at least in the laboratory, created organic out of inorganic materials. Cosmic radiation striking an oxygen-poor atmosphere on the early earth could have produced the organic milieu, the setting for the first life on earth.

Then, in 1953, Dr. Stanley L. Miller, while a graduate student at the University of Chicago working under Dr. Harold C. Urey, sent an electrical discharge through a mixture of gases that probably more closely simulated earth's original atmosphere — methane, ammonia, water vapor, and hydrogen. The electrical discharge was a lightning bolt scaled down to laboratory size. The lightning produced amino acids, the building blocks of complex proteins, which are the basic constituents of living matter.

Since then, Miller's results have been corroborated and many more inquiries have been made on nucleic acids, viruses, photosynthesis, and protein structure to bridge the gap between inanimate and animate matter. Most of the research workers involved believe now that lightning, radiation, or heat alone enriched the chemicals in earth's primeval seas or on the surface of the land, and they gradually changed under their own power into complex compounds. These combined with each other to form even larger molecules, leading to giant ones capable of reproducing themselves. At exactly what point these molecules are worthy of the definition "life" is uncertain. It may be only a matter of size. Or it may not matter.

Dr. Sidney W. Fox, director of the Institute of Molecular Evolution, University of Miami, and his co-workers have shown that, contrary to prior scientific opinion, heat alone is sufficient for primordial synthesis. Imitating geothermal conditions of the primeval earth in the laboratory, they were able to produce 14 of the 18 amino acids found in protein and to condense all the amino acids into polymers that have many of the properties of proteins. One of these properties is the tendency to form structured units similar to biological cells. These results have now been confirmed in other laboratories.

The work is significant because it indicates that, while amino acids may have formed in a variety of ways, probably the *only* way proteins could have begun was through the action of heat, and not of lightning or cosmic rays. Of greater importance, Fox has shown how the self-organizing properties of the thermal polyamino acids would yield a primitive cell. He has discovered how many of the properties of living cells — such as fissionability and double layers — could be incorporated into these units spontaneously under geologically plausible conditions.

Fox suggests that life may be beginning continuously on earth, even now, despite the absence of a methane or high carbon dioxide atmosphere. "The common floral pattern of many hot springs areas and concepts of parallel evolution are consistent with this idea," he said, "and pose the possibility that we fail to recognize life beginning anew because it so resembles unevolved descendants of primitive forms already here."

The idea is contrary to views stated several decades ago by the famous Russian biochemist A. I. Oparin. He believed that the oxygen now in our air would oxidize the tender molecular aggregates that aspire to life, and the now-existent bacteria would kill them. Fox, however, believes "we have less reason to exclude the possibility of life beginning now on earth than we had formerly."

Of all the sciences, only the study of life, or biology, has not benefited from comparisons with the universe beyond earth—as have physics, chemistry, and the other "physical" sciences. Is it not reasonable to suppose that breakthroughs might be made in biology on the basis of comparisons with life from other worlds? Have organisms elsewhere found alternative solutions to processes we think of as basic scientific principles? Can we hope to understand "life" even before we can define it?

If life on other worlds, different in chemical or morphological structure or function were found, our idea of "living things" would be altered drastically.

Sister Mary Cecilia Bodman, professor of evolution at Mundelein College, Chicago, comments: "If living things were found that lacked the key characteristics we now use to identify a living thing, how should we identify them as living? I find this a completely impossible philosophical position. I am more frustrated than the farmer when he first saw a giraffe and said, 'There ain't no such animal!' "

While understanding of life is such an enormous concept that it may never be completed, understanding of how living things evolve from the inanimate seems at least to be within our immediate grasp. A "unified theory" of evolution, from the formation of molecules in space to stars to planets to living systems to intelligence to — possibly — a purpose of the universe, is the grand prize, the ultimate goal of scientific inquiry.

Dr. Lawrence B. Slobodkin, zoology professor at the University of Michigan, derides the "irresistible temptation" for biologists and non-biologists alike to find some point, purpose, or goal in the evolutionary process. He believes philosophical conclusions about the ultimate meaning of evolution are not weaknesses of biological theory. They are not due to a shortage of biological facts. "They are simply wrong," he states. "Evolution, in fact, is only a consequence of the general homeostatic ability of organisms combined with the biochemical properties of genetic material."

Be that as it may, we still should ask, what is the purpose of homeostasis or of persistence? That is, what is the purpose of creation, of life, of death?

It may take thousands of years for terrestrial science to answer these questions if they are answerable by science at all. Here we come to the potentially most exciting prospect of extraterrestrial investigations, the learning from intelligent life elsewhere.

Just knowing that man is not alone in the universe would change our outlook considerably. But actually communicating with other civilizations would be a breakthrough equal to countless years of scientific study in all spheres of knowledge. I will not dwell on the many questions we might ask of *homo superiors,* questions of the universe, of creation, of immortality, or the upsettingly simple answers we might get to questions unasked, the gaps of theory that might be bridged, or the variety of ways the information might be transmitted. These propositions have been written into several thousand provocative science fiction stories ranging from Plato to Huxley and are there for your stimulus.

Rather, I would like to explain why any BEMs* *we may talk to* are smarter than we are and why science fiction writers call them BEMs.

The first answer involves the likelihood that any civilization sufficiently advanced to have discovered radio, sufficiently resourceful to beam it some light-years distant in our direction, and sufficiently interested to spend whatever they use for money on such projects must at least rival us in our scientific and technological capability. (Conversely, contact is effectively screened from lesser civilizations.) If a civilization is at least as technically advanced as ours, chances are it will be several thousand years further along. The coincidence of coming into radio contact with intelligent life in another star system within anything less than 10,000 years of our evolutionary stage is a staggering improbability.

I introduce the fictional term "BEM" not to belittle extraterrestrials, but to awaken the many scientists who, upon admitting the possibility that planets exist at other stars, cautiously admit that life may exist on such planets, and then, more hesitantly, if life — then — possibly — intelligent life.

An acronym in wide use among science fiction fans standing for "Bug-Eyed Monsters," or intelligent life vastly different from us.

Three-bodied BEM on a triple star system planet poses in a trium-
virate of Why not?

Having gone that far seems far enough. They feel a desperate need to draw the line somewhere short of the stuff of science fiction. They insist therefore that if extraterrestrial intelligence does exist, it surely came about as it did here, that is, by hydrocarbon evolution from the lower animals to the familiar primate with opposed thumbs.

Those scientists who have decided that all life must be carbonaceous and that all sentient life must take the human form are as guilty of anthropocentrism as Ptolemy. They reason not as scientists, but as birds. Bird-reasoners are convinced that air at 760 torr, containing 21% oxygen, and at temperatures between 0 and 100 F, is essential for flapping, breathing, and laying eggs. They are right—for terrestrial birds. But what bird-reasoner who never saw a fish, for instance, could envision an animal that has neither wings nor legs and breathes oxygen out of a liquid compressed so densely as to crush any self-respecting fowl?

Science fictionists, on the other hand, fondly refer to other intelligences as BEMs because of a deep-seated belief that the infinite variety of life on this one planet must be repeated in resounding polyphony throughout the habitable universe.

Why?

Simply because they extrapolate. They see the animate product of the only world they know as the hordes of swimming, crawling, walking, flying creatures, the sedentary bacteria and fungi, the algae, grasses, and trees that clothe the earth in green and brown, filling every corner of the land from equator to pole, from sea bottom to mountain peak. They have seen condors as high as $5\frac{1}{2}$ miles in the Andes; they have dredged up animals that phosphoresce their own light from homes in the ocean depths where pressures rival those on Jupiter, only then helplessly to watch them explode in our rarified alien environment. They have found dark green lichens in the bitter-cold ice crevasses at the south pole, stubbornly surviving and adapting so the next generation, perhaps, finds survival easier. The lesson we learn on earth is that nature adapts life to environment.

Astronomer Kenneth Heuer, formerly of the American Museum, Hayden Planetarium, New York, suggests that "we think poorly of nature's power when we consider as utterly uninhabitable those worlds with different environments."

It is difficult for me to accept the idea that intelligence is a statistical accident, as George G. Simpson, professor of vertebrate paleontology at the Museum of Comparative Zoology, Harvard University, would have us believe. But I concur wholeheartedly with his concept that the form of the creature into the ambulating, arm-swinging biped called man *is* an accident. In his book, "This View of Life: the World of an Evolutionist," Simpson says:

"Even slight changes in earlier parts of the [evolutionary] history would have profound cumulative effects on all descendant organisms through the succeeding millions of generations. In spite of the enormous diversity of life, with many millions of species through the years, it represents only a minute fraction of the possible forms of life. The existing species would surely have been different if the start had been different and if any stage of the histories of organisms and their environments had been different. Thus the existence of our present species depends on a very precise sequence of causative events through some 2-billion years or more. Man cannot be an exception to this rule. If the causal chain had been different, *homo sapiens* would not exist."

But Simpson concludes that it is "extremely unlikely that anything enough like us for real communication of thought exists anywhere in our accessible universe." What pessimism from a man who says he enjoys reading science fiction and whose conclusions leave him "with a feeling almost of sorrow!" There is one beautiful answer that should cheer Simpson. Biologists are prone to forget it, but astronomers can not: *Even improbable events become inevitable on the cosmic time and quantity scale of the universe.*

Dinosaurs, as Simpson says, are gone forever. And man is not repeatable. But intelligence need not be the heritage of apes alone; it ought to be repeatable in other form.

Nor is this concept unlikely or even teleological. Intelligence could have evolved here from a dinosaur or a dog—or from the garbage of some careless explorer who found no one home on earth 2½-billion years ago.

Elsewhere life might be as universal as it is on this planet, and just as adapted to the ambient chemical compounds and temperature. Biochemist and science fictionist Dr. Isaac Asimov, of the Boston University Medical School, has suggested these possibilities: life based upon fluorine and silicon at temperatures hot enough to make iron glow; fluorocarbon life, with liquid sulfur taking the place of water at more moderate high temperatures, from 300 to 800 F; liquid ammonia life at temperatures around −100 F; life based on liquid methane on planets where −260 F are normal (a cartoon shows a BEM recently crashed on a desert planet struggling across the landscape, uttering from somewhere behind a parched tongue the words: "Methane! Methane!"); and, even, liquid hydrogen serving as the universal, liquid solvent at temperatures near absolute zero.

Less "conventional" speculations also may be made. Somewhere in the universe, life may exist beyond the analogies of chemical-temperature systems. Holy Ghosts may have counterparts in ghosts less holy. Our own universe may be but an electron in the atom of something larger. Or life in this universe, this galaxy, or even this corner of a spiral arm may have sprung from a light beam in the presence of a suitably catalyzed hydrogen atom. Or from a force of energy in space animate and alive in every sense: metabolizing, emoting, reproducing, adapting, and communicating intelligently by its own radio waves to other similar creatures lightyears distant. Such a living thing need have no planetary base, no requirement for water, ammonia, or methane. It might extend over millions of miles from "head to tail;" it might live as many years as it is miles long, or fail to differentiate between individual and race, thus achieving immortality in a single being.

Asimov's BEMs are only speculative parallels to life as it exists on earth. Mine are only speculative nonparallels. Both are included here for a single reason: to ask the reader to consider the definition of intelligent life.

A quick run-down on the various psychologists' definitions of intelligence seems to include: the ability to perceive one's environment, to deal with it symbolically, to adjust to it, and/or to work toward a goal. An equally fast survey of biologists' definitions of life includes the following verbs: to replicate, metabolize, grow, emote, reproduce, and, together with others of your race, to evolve.

But it is easy to find exceptions to these and other definitions designed to cover the variety of things on earth that seem to be alive and seem to be intelligent. Almost 3-billion apparently intelligent life forms exist on this planet, not counting dolphins. Yet they neither know where they come from nor where they are going, except generally away from the star Vega, at 12 miles a second. By the definition of some really advanced BEM elsewhere, intelligence may not exist on earth, which would explain why we haven't been contacted—

or why we can't recognize that we have been!

Conversely, it also is easy to envision man-built self-organizing systems — tomorrow's computers, perceptrons, or homeostats—doing all of the intelligent- and life-defined things except, perhaps, displaying emotions (although, why not code desire, dread, etc. into their mechanistic DNA-equivalent circuits?) If I listen correctly, psychological theory seems to be saying that mere interpretation of your environment doesn't make you intelligent; you have to deal with it symbolically. And biological theory seems to say that merely reproducing yourself doesn't make you alive; you have to have fun doing it!

Clearly, our definitions and horizons need amplification from other worlds. If BEMs, intelligent or otherwise, await us in space, how shall we find them?

Mars and Venus seem to be the closest places to look for extraterrestrial life. Yet 12.5% of a representative sample of the nation's biologists who care about such matters don't rule out the possibility of microorganisms on the moon existing in some subselenian, completely encapsulated, perhaps volcanic, pocket.

Asked if they believed there is a possibility that water may be found on the moon, 25% of those who answered the biology questionnaire said "yes," 46.4% "no," and 28.6% "no opinion." Half of that quarter who gave hope for lunar water also believe life could exist on the moon. If not lunar life, perhaps fragments of the precursors of "original life" may be found in meteorites on the moon. Such remnants are lost to us on earth, having interacted with our atmosphere.

The concensus of concerned biologists is that the moon is barren of life, but that it has four other biologic reasons for development: (1) as an other-world laboratory to study transplanted microbes, plants, and animals including man; (2) as a sanitarium for the infirm (who can afford it); (3) as a low-gravity, no-atmosphere base for more economical and more frequent unmanned or manned life-searching missions to Mars and the other planets; and (4) as a far-side base for interception of radio or light signals from extrasolar system intelligences. These biological uses of the moon will be discussed in turn.

The biologists surveyed expressed interest in the possibility of growing bacteria under lunar conditions and all kinds of plants under various induced atmospheres. Biological experiments of many kinds require a sterile environment, which is illimitable on the moon (unless Lunik and Ranger germs somehow survived and multiplied!).

While sterile atmospheres can be made on earth, conditions of low gravity can not. Would vegetables grow tall or more fruitful under one-sixth "g" conditions? Would the 350-hour unbroken daytime of artificially diffused sunlight, in combination with low gravity and a high plant-optimum carbon dioxide atmosphere, simplify the otherwise difficult problems of producing food and oxygen for the lunar base?

The lunar gravity is low; somewhere between the moon and earth gravity is zero. Both conditions should be studied. It is strange that almost no emphasis has been given in the scientific literature to distinguish between the "zero g" of an artificial earth satellite— where centrifugal forces of rotation counterbalance the still prominent gravitational attraction of the earth— and the true zero g far from any world. These are presumed to be nearly equivalent, but only because we're applying our earthly experience.

The effects of the very different day-night cycle and its possible changes within human organs that control sleeping and waking, hunger, body temperature swings, and cell growth can be studied uniquely on the moon—as can unshielded solar and cosmic radiation on biological systems.

Approximating weightlessness on earth is imperfect simulation at best. In underwater photograph above, "astronaut" makes a simulated trip in space through a tunnel connecting two "space vehicles." Water in his "spacesuit" reduces the astronaut's buoyancy to approximately zero. At right, centrifuge is used to test astronaut's adaptability to twice normal gravity, encountered in rocketship launchings. Low "g" condition on the moon may prove to be an asset for plant growth, as a hospital for cardiac patients, and for study of other biological processes.

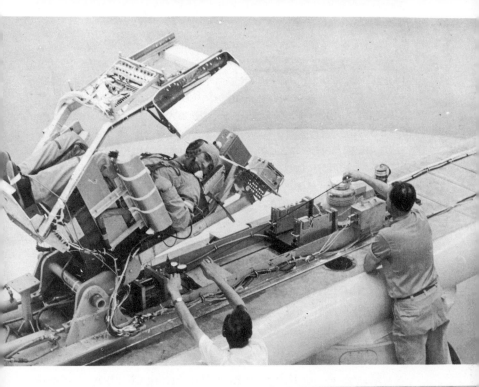

The moon as a hospital for cardiac patients is another reason for lunar development that has been both extensively ridiculed and defended. Only 27.8% of surveyed biologists thought the moon ever could have a hospital use. It does seem a very long-range application of the moon, one that probably will not be considered seriously until the end of the century.

Certainly the low gravity will attract hospitals of the future: lunar gravity might permit weakened hearts, other muscles, or organs of the body to function more easily, or allow broken bones to mend faster. More likely, it would be considerably easier for the infirm to move about on the moon; cripples confined to wheelchairs on earth might walk again inside a lunar sanitarium where a 168-pound man would weigh but 28 pounds.

The big question is an engineering one—could an elderly or sick patient survive the trip?

There is nothing inherently rugged about space travel; even automobiles were too vigorous for some people when they first were made. In the time to come, as relatively unlimited nuclear energy is harnessed for moonships, near-horizontal takeoffs and gentle accelerations to escape-velocity should become feasible.

Some of the biologists answering the hospital question state categorically that "no human life is worth the expense." (I wonder if they include their own?) In stark, shuddering contrast is physicist Robert C. W. Ettinger's book, "The Prospect for Immortality," which develops a rationale for deep-freezing all newly dead corpses and rejuvenating them at a later date when mankind learns to cure the sickness it calls death. If Ettinger manages to find sufficient support for his project (which is doubtful since all investigators in the field of reduced metabolism consider his proposal preposterous), we have a massive new use for the darkened, cold crater bottoms and polar areas of the moon.

I should go into business with Ettinger; the lunar cryostat described in Capter III would find enormous application with the current production of 3-billion corpses every half century and a death rate that gives evidence of doubling every 37 years!

At these exponents for both the dead and the living, there had better be billions of unpopulated planets, for we shall need them. The horror of unchecked immortality makes even death easier to take.

Moonships to Venus, Mars, and the asteroid belt make more immediate sense for the development of the moon. Scores of plans for low "g" launchings have been devised in which the moon serves as a large close-to-home spaceship base. For greater economy and efficiency, vehicles would be true spaceships, plying the void between moon and the natural or artificial satellites of the planets and never entering an atmosphere. Rather than describe these engineering marvels portrayed so often in the newspapers, let's discuss the current state of exobiological exploration.

The Mariner series of instrumented spacecraft both hastens the eventual development of the moon as a rocket-launching site and, meanwhile, shortcuts the way to knowledge of the plants.

Venus, the closest planet, was probed first during a favorable opposition in 1962, as was explained in the last chapter, and temporarily shattered speculation about earth-type Venusians by measuring temperatures of the order of 800 F. Before Mariner II and after the Johns Hopkins' high-altitude balloon experiments two years later, anything on Venus went, and goes, including prehistoric-type monsters lurking behind blue icebergs, or a planet covered entirely by water with luxurious tropical plants swaying under warm seas.

Even should future measurements confirm surface temperatures above the boiling point of water, they would not necessarily deny the existence of life on

Venus. Intelligent Venusians could be Asimov fluorocarbonic creatures. If you look imaginatively at that retrograde planet, you see them drinking evening cocktails of liquid sulfur while watching the sun sink slowly in the east.

Yet even terrestrial-type (carbon-oxygen) Venusians may exist. Birds, insects, and microbial spores could live out their lives in the dense higher atmosphere where water vapor may exist at more comfortable temperatures.

It is difficult to leave that mystery land for the rusted desert of Mars, despite the fact that we know considerably more about conditions on the red planet. Our first robot envoy, Mariner IV, enroute Marsward since Nov. 28, 1964, and the Soviet's Zond II, hurled two days later, are to have approached Mars during July, 1965. If successful (this writing is prior to the estimated date of arrival), they will televise close-up pictures of the *surface* of another planet for the first time in history. The pictures and measurements would give us a better idea of the amount of carbon dioxide, oxygen, water vapor, and other constituents of the Martian atmosphere; confirm or deny the existence of widespread vegetation that seems to darken parts of the planet seasonally; explain Schiaparelli's "canali" (he meant "channels," not "canals," incidentally), thereby ending an 88-year spree of speculation; and tell us whether the polar caps are truly ice or, instead, oxides of nitrogen as has been proposed recently. Other Mariner instruments are designed to reveal whether Mars has a magnetic field and, if so, whether it also possesses the equivalent of the earth's Van Allen belts of trapped radiation. If it does not, life would be considerably restricted since the intensity of cosmic rays would be too great to allow anything but elemental life forms to evolve.

Whatever Mariner IV, Zond II, or similar flybys

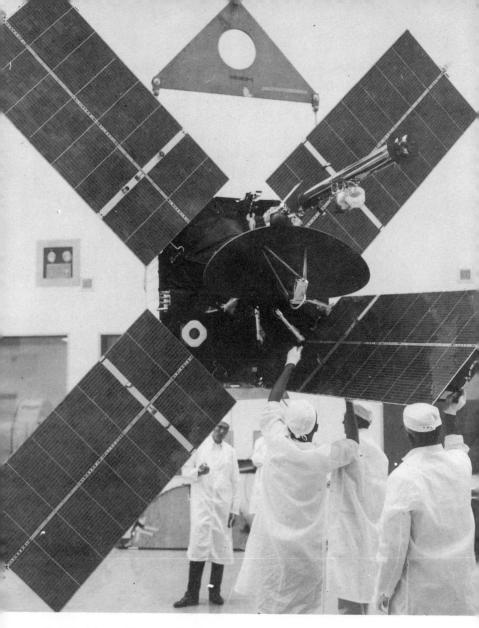

Robot ship to Mars — Mariner IV — looked like this at Jet Propulsion Laboratory before it was launched. Four "paddle wheels" are solar panels that convert the sun's heat into electricity. Mariner IV's July, 1965 televised photographs of the red planet were first close-ups of another planet's surface. (Mariner II photographed Venus, but saw only its clouds.)

tell us about plant life on Mars, a covey of life detectors is being prepared now to hit the Martian surface about the time man lands on the moon. NASA now is deciding whether to launch the first Voyager landing mission in the favorable oppositions of 1969, 1971, or 1973. The 1971 Mars "window" is open the widest: the two planets will be less than 35-million miles apart at that time and the Martian spring and summer will be in full bloom so that the possibly-biological "waves of darkening" can be studied.

Most of the life detectors operate on the earth-correct theory that microorganisms make up an important portion of the Martian biosphere. For instance, "Gulliver," brainchild of Dr. Gilbert V. Levine, Hazleton Laboratories Inc., Falls Church, Va., is based on the detection of metabolic end-products from organisms grown in a radioisotope-tagged medium. Landed on Mars, the instrument would explosively shoot three sticky strings out as far as 50 feet. As the strings are reeled back into a nutrient broth, they carry along particles of soil and, perhaps, microorganisms.

If bacteria are present, they will grow in the "hot" broth and eventually evolve radioactive metabolic gases. These will be collected, the radioactivity measured at intervals with a transistorized Geiger counter, and the information radioed back to earth.

Gas evolving at an exponential rate would indicate growth. The presence of more than one exponential phase would signify that multiple organisms are active. Even if no growth occurs during the experiment, Gulliver still could detect metabolism. Gulliver is the furthest developed of this group of life instruments.

Another technique from Hazleton Laboratories, called "Diogenes," is based on the reaction between certain chemicals and adenosine triphosphate (ATP)—a material found in almost all terrestrial life. ATP and oxygen will cause substances like those found in fireflies, luciferin and luciferase, to emit light. This mixture, lacking only the ATP, could be exposed to the Martian environment; bioluminescent activity would infer life.

"Wolftrap," cleverly named for the famous nature photographer and biologist, Dr. Wolf Vishniac of the University of Rochester, also is designed to detect the presence of bacteria. A fragile vacuum tube probe would shatter when Wolftrap hit the Martian surface, sucking soil onto prepared culture plates. Suitable detectors would indicate changes in turbidity, or cloudiness, of the culture media due to bacterial growth. An increase in the acidity of the nutrient broth, measured with a simple pH indicator, also could be used as an index of microorganism activity.

"Multivator" is one of several life detectors designed by Nobelist Dr. Joshua Lederberg, who heads the department of genetics at Stanford University's School of Medicine. This one cunningly reports on the presence of a very widespread enzyme called phosphatase—which almost certainly would indicate carbon-based life. Colorimetric measurements (based on the intensity of color in a solution) or fluorometric analysis (a measurement of the fluorescent light emitted by a sample) would be used to learn whether enzyme reactions take place in samples of Martian dust.

Dust particles from the Martian surface would be vacuum-drawn into the instrument and the solids dissolved in a reaction chamber (see diagram on next page). The resultant solution then would be analyzed for color or fluorescence using suitable light sources, filters, and a light-detecting photomultiplier tube. As with the other robot explorers, a radio link with the earth would allow analysis of the data.

Philco Corp. biochemists at the company's Aeronutronic Division, assuming that Mars evolved as did earth and that primeval life forms were protein-cen-

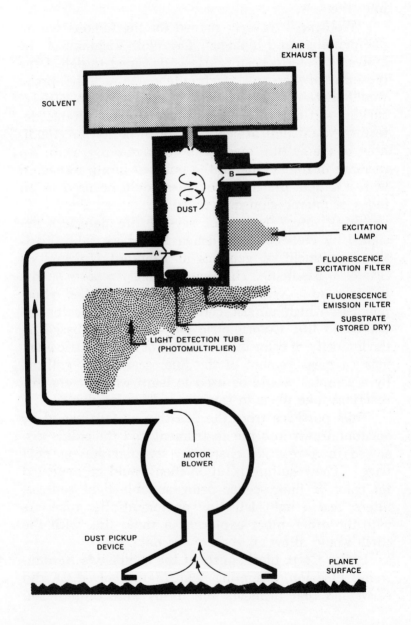

AIR
EXHAUST

SOLVENT

DUST

B

EXCITATION
LAMP

A

FLUORESCENCE
EXCITATION FILTER

FLUORESCENCE
EMISSION FILTER

SUBSTRATE
(STORED DRY)

LIGHT DETECTION TUBE
(PHOTOMULTIPLIER)

MOTOR
BLOWER

DUST PICKUP
DEVICE

PLANET
SURFACE

tered, have developed a "J-Band" life detector. The "J" comes from E. E. Jelly, a photographic scientist who showed that dibenzothiocarbocyanine dye exhibits an intense and unusual spectral peak in certain wavelength bands when absorbed onto a macromolecule.

For example, the dye will change color when it is absorbed on the large protein molecule. Other life-indicating macromolecules, such as DNA or certain carbohydrates, will cause different spectral changes when they pick up the dye. Detectors—visual spectrometers—sensing these variations in color, would radio the news to earth.

Scientists at the Jet Propulsion Laboratory feel that no experiments have been proposed to detect extra-terrestrial life without strong assumptions about the nature of that life. Thus, they champion a combined gas chromatography-mass spectrometry technique which can detect and identify life-related chemical compounds with minimum speculation about the life itself. Even so, carbon-based organisms are assumed and the total absence of organics would indicate a "negative" result.

In addition to these approaches, biological microscopes linked to television cameras, optical rotation instruments, and numerous other analytical devices are being developed to test the Martian soil or atmosphere for signs of life. NASA hopes to include the best of the many ingenious life detectors in its ABL Mars mission, scheduled to land two 5,000-pound *Automated Biological Laboratories* on the red planet sometime between 1969 and 1973.

When all of this robot work is done, we still may not know conclusively whether life exists on other solar system planets. Some critic certainly will claim that the wiggly thing detected by Gulliver or Multivator was carried there from earth on equipment that somehow escaped complete sterilization. Men are necessary on Mars just as they are on the moon to answer the tens of thousands of questions that will become significantly evident. In the last analysis, man may turn out to be not only the best instrument for space probing, but the cheapest as well.

The manned search for life on the planets need not be concerned only with present life. Some hypotheses of planetary formation say that Venus, being closer to the sun, is earlier than earth in its evolutionary development. Earth, it follows, is earlier than Mars.

Thus, interplanetary flights may be rewarded richly: on the moon we may learn whether meteors can bridge the void from one planet to another, perhaps seeding worlds as bees do flowers; on Venus we may find life in formation and learn how it is generated from the inanimate; on Mars the remnants of an ancient civilization may be fossilized in those red rocks.

Life beyond the earth is intoxicating fare, and even conservative scientists can get carried away (a promising sign!). In 1959, I. Shklovski, a Soviet astrophysicist who is (still) widely respected, suggested with tongue only part way in cheek that the tiny moons of Mars were artificial satellites launched by an advanced civilization. The innermost, Phobos, only 3,500 miles from its primary, is at the critical limit of instability and brushes the Martian atmosphere. Observations of its acceleration (according to most but not all astronomers) have shown that it will fall to Mars in a mere 10-million years or less.

But there is insufficient atmosphere that high above Mars to account for the cosmically rapid braking; nor can it be due to tidal action.

Shklovski sought to account for the Phobos fall by suggesting that it was *hollow,* since it would have to be of negligible mass to be braked by the rarified Martian atmosphere. If hollow, he said, it might be artificial too, and the reason both Deimos and Phobos had not been detected before 1877 was for the excellent reason that they had not yet been launched! The idea is fun and cannot be disproved, yet. Unfortunately, it is not very plausible because any Martian civilization capable of launching artificial satellites of 5- and 10-mile diameters in 1877 also should have been capable of visiting or at least communicating with earth. A more plausible explanation for intelligence-on-Mars enthusiasts is that the satellites were launched some millions of years ago when the fourth planet was at a similar evolutionary stage as the third is now. And it wasn't until the favorable opposition of earth and Mars in 1877, as well as the development of superior telescopes, that they were observed.

More disappointing, but infinitely more likely, is the explanation offered by cosmologist A. Dauvillier. His ideas were explained at some length in the last chapter in preference to the dozens of other better-known cosmogonic theories, because they are startlingly complete and relatively unknown in this country. Dauvillier's belief is that Phobos was fragmented a long time ago on its way from the asteroid belt—the ultimate evolutionary fate of all asteroids—and now consists of a swarm of small bodies whose apparent volume is a thousand times greater than its mass.

The reference to inanimate evolution is deliberate. Charles Darwin's century old "revolution of evolution" was a milestone in human self-comprehension. Now we see the theory begins too late with the emergence of life. The current product—certainly not the end product—of that evolution, the human brain, requires it to begin further back, at the beginnings of planets, of stars, of galaxies, of creation.

The distinguished British astronomer Fred Hoyle believes man is not free from evolutionary processes even now, that the competition merely has changed from that between men and the lesser animals to that between men with ideas in conflict with men with other ideas. Hoyle suggests that we are living neither in the long primitive era nor in a better-adjusted prosperous future.

We are in the middle, in a transitional phase of maximum strain.

Because we live in this special phase we find social difficulties, pressures, situations that defy even the simplest logical processes. We are not in contact with the forces that shape the future; we are not in charge of our own destiny; the emergence of intelligence on earth has changed the ground-rules of evolution.

Should we discover how to communicate with intelligent extraterrestrials, we will evolve at a faster rate and "mutations of ideas" will occur. Like genetic mutations, most new concepts turn out badly, but without mutations there can be no evolution, and without new ideas we will stagnate.

Dr. Philip Morrison and Dr. G. Cocconi of Cornell University speculate that an interchange of messages is taking place on a vast scale, all the time, but that we are as unaware of it as a pygmy in the African forests is unaware of the radio messages that flash at the speed of light around the earth. There might be a million or more subscribers in the galactic directory.

It would be useful to know exactly what is going to happen if mankind continues its present world policies. What courses of action lead to nuclear war? Which avoid it? How do we solve the impending over-population crisis? A shortcut to these answers lies in a question we have only ourselves to ask:

If it exists, how do we get our name into Morrison's galactic directory?

Many astute assumptions as to frequencies and codes that extraterrestrials might use have been discussed ever since "Project Ozma" began in 1960 at the

National Radio Astronomy Observatory in Green Bank, W.Va. Cornell University astronomer Frank Drake used the 85-foot radio telescope there to listen to the radio outpouring of the relatively near stars Tau Ceti and Epsilon Eridani. But the noise appeared to be only noise. Moreover, the Green Bank telescope is too insensitive to detect any but signals beamed directly at earth. And the project lasted only a few months—less than a speck of time in the millions of years interstellar signaling might have been going on—even assuming intelligent BEMs had any reason to pick the sun from among billions of stars to which to beam their messages.

Drake has reasoned that interstellar broadcasters might use the 1420 megacycle band. Since hydrogen atoms emit a small amount of energy at this frequency, and since hydrogen constitutes the vast majority of matter in the universe, the 1420 band may be considered to be universal among beings who have mastered radio. If they do beam at this frequency, they may send pulses indicating numbers that mean something—such as the number for pi or, better, the number for the "fine structure constant."

This dimensionless number represents the ratio of the wavelength of light emitted by hydrogen, certain factors involved in sustaining a nuclear chain reaction, the circumference of the orbit of the hydrogen electron, and several other relationships in atomic physics. Scientists know only the first six digits of the fine structure constant: 137,039. The more decimal places to which extraterrestrials were to carry this number in a transmission to earth, the greater would be the evidence of their scientific superiority.

The piling of assumptions gets a little sticky here. First, we have to assume that radio signals are being sent, in preference to an advanced form of something akin to light beams from lasers, or in preference to other as yet undiscovered energies of communication.

Second, we have to assume the frequency to be 1420 megacycles or some other "logical" frequency. Third, we assume the signals are sent from intelligent beings sufficiently related to earth man in thought so that we can recognize their signals as intelligent. Fourth, we assume a sufficiently large telescope to receive these signals from a variety of areas in space. And fifth, we assume that this type of listening activity would remain nonderided and funded for at least several hundred years. If all these conditions were met, we might then have some infinitesimal chance for success.

We should take that chance.

In addition, we should take a less passive approach. Hoyle suggests construction of a huge saucer-like metal mirror at least the size of the 1,000-foot antenna in Puerto Rico, but with the steerable precision of the 210-foot Australian radio telescope. Such an instrument, preferably placed on the moon's far side to eliminate terrestrial radio interference, would make it possible to *transmit* an intelligible message as far as the nearest star, about four lightyears away. By increasing the output by a factor of only ten, we then could reach the nearest thousand stars; by 100, the nearest million. "Somewhere among these," Hoyle believes, "is the neighbor we are looking for."

A similar estimate, by Nobelist Edward Purcell of Harvard University, indicates that two 300-foot radio telescopes—one a transmitter, the other a receiver—could communicate over a distance of 500 lightyears. Some 2,000 stars similar to the sun are included in that range.

Our plans for interstellar transmission may never be that ambitious since we would have to wait 500 years between question and answer! But cosmic conversation across 40 lightyears or so might well be considered. And we need not send one fact or one question to await an answer. Volumes of data could be transmitted con-

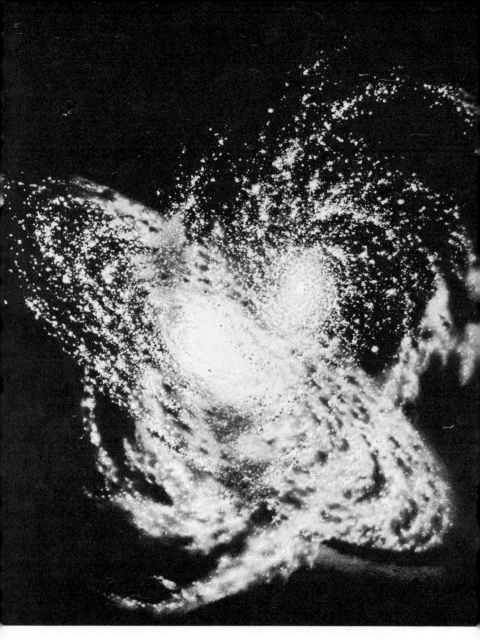

Collision of galaxies, depicted in painting by Antonio Petruccelli, shows how interstellar spiral arms would interact while individual stars themselves remain unaffected. Somewhere out there, there may be intelligent life. An astronomical base on the moon would help us find it.

tinuously, for our children to inherit similar volumes beginning four-score years later.

Whatever the distances involved, it seems clear that if we want to increase the infinitesimal chances of communicating with extraterrestrial intelligences we need to do more than just listen. Undoubtedly we will learn considerably more about the planets in our own system once telescopes of even moderate size are put into operation on the moon. The opportunities of receiving from and transmitting signals to other star systems are much better on the moon where the entire electromagnetic spectrum is open and—more important—where radio interference from earth can be cancelled.

Laser beams, pulsed according to one of the numbers-that-mean-something originally conceived for listening purposes, could be used for transmission from a lunar base. If laser communication systems are feasible only in space, as was suggested in the Cambridge Research Laboratories report referred to in Chapter VI, then a post on the moon becomes even more essential for interstellar communication plans.

Someday, perhaps soon, lasers may make better sense than radio beams for this purpose. No known "natural" source in space emits laser waves. A laser beam of light from the vicinity of earth would stand out clearly from background radiation, signaling to the universe that we are ready to join Morrison's club. Further, a laser can be focused more precisely than a radio beam since its beam width is narrower.

Unfortunately, you can't put as much power into a laser as you can into a radio, and the light from any laser so far built could not be seen from even the closest star. Yet we must remember that lasers were invented just a few years ago! Given time—and the desire—we may expect new breakthroughs to occur quickly, at least paralleling the rapid development of radio and its many electronic offspring.

Admittedly, these speculations of communicating with beings whose existence we can only surmise are as "far out" as you can get. Admittedly, they are for future generations to accomplish. Yet the legacy we leave our children, or our great-great-grandchildren, ought to concern us today as we take the first cosmically tiny step toward the moon.

That step leads not only to other worlds. It leads to other worlds of thought, to an awakening that cannot be described, to a renaissance without human parallel.

Really, that renaissance is what going to the moon is all about.

index

Black dwarfs, 199
Bodman, Sister Maria Cecilia, 205
Boeing Co., The, 126
Bolometers, 40
Bonding, 135
Boric acid, 99
Boron, 97, 99
Bottles, condiment, analogy of, 142
Brazing, 48
Bricks, 85, 105
"Bridges," intergalactic, 189-90
Bromine, 97
Brown, Dr. Harrison, 198-99
Brown Engineering Co., Inc., 130
Brunetti, Dr. Cledo, 39
Bulge, great lunar, 110

Cadmium, 34, 97
Cadmium selenide, 40
Cadmium sulfide, 40
"Caille iron," 101
Calcite, 94
Calcium, 101
California, University of, 93, 193, 202
Caltech, 178, 199
Calvin, Dr. Melvin, 202
Cambridge Research Laboratories, 168
Canals on Mars, 218
Cancer, 1, 9, 10, 201
Capacitors, 39, 76, 139, 140
Cape Kennedy, 151
Captured-planet theory, 107-8, 110
Carbohydrates, 223
Carbon, 31, 53, 135, 139, 208ff.
  C₂, 92-93
  meteoritic, 101, 102, 103, 105
Carbon dioxide, 99, 204, 213, 218
Carbon monoxide, 86
Carbon steel, 51
Cardiac patients, 216
Castings, 47, 48, 103
Catalysts, 94
Catapults, launching, 68, 69, 70
Cathode-ray tubes, 76, 130-31
Cathodic sputtering, 27-28
Cesium, 159
Chemical milling, 134
Chemicals, 47, 66, 85
  See also specific chemicals
Chemists, 3, 115, 116, 120-21
Chicago Tribune, 5-6
Chicago, University of, 105, 193, 202
Chick embryos, 124-26
Chlorine, 97
Chondrites, 102, 105
Chondrules, 102, 108
Chromatography, gas, 223
Chromium, 99-101, 137
Chromosphere, 174
Ci-2354, 197
Cigar sorting, 140
Cigarettes, 9
Cinnabar, 96
Circuits and circuitry, 25, 26, 38-39,
  76, 130, 140
Civil defense, 130
Clarke, Arthur C., 14n, 69, 70
Cleaning of surfaces, 24

Clouds,
  dust-cloud theory, 108, 109, 178-79,
    186-87
  intergalactic, 189-90
  seeding of, 169
Coating, 30-31, 47, 53-54, 76
Cobalt, 96, 99, 103
Cocconi, Dr. G., 226
Cold, 77, 123-24
  See also Temperature
Colds, common, 1
Cole, Dandridge M., 70-71, 94
Colloids, 83
Columbia University, 7
Columbus, Christopher, 14, 46
Combustion liners, 137
Comets, 180
Committee on Utilization of Scientific
  and Engineering Manpower, 11
Common cold, the, 1
Communications, 34, 51, 54, 122, 139,
  166-68, 225-31
Components, 38-39, 46ff., 130-33
  See also specific components, types
  of components
Computers, 14n, 25ff., 76, 130, 133-34
Condors, 208
Conductivity, 30, 36, 40, 141
  See also Semiconductors ;
  Superconductivity ; etc.
Congress, 5-9, 43, 72
Connectors, 130
Continuous Lunar Coater, 53-54, 76
Converters, energy, 41, 47, 72, 122-23
Cook Electric Co., 168
Copernicus (crater), 112
Copper, 30, 48, 94, 99, 101
  in meteorites, 103
  in ocean deposits, 96
  welding, 51
Cornell University, 105, 179, 226, 227
Corona, solar, 31, 174-76
Corpses, freezing, 216-17
Corrosion, 31
Craters, moon, 62, 81ff.
Craters of the Moon National
  Monument, 87
Crimean Astrophysical Observatory, 97
Cripples, 216
Crucibles, 139
Cryobiology, 36-38
Cryogenic devices, 123-24
  See also Vacuum, use of ; specific
  devices
Cryonetics Corp., 66
Cryostat, lunar, 36, 56, 57-63, 217
Crystals, 28, 48
Cyclotrons, 40

Darwin, Charles, 225
Darwin, G. H., 106
Dating, radioactive, 110
Dauvillier, Prof. A., 109, 186-89,
  190, 225
Days, lunar, 55ff., 213
DC-3 aircraft, 16
Dead, deep-freezing of, 216-17
Dearborn Observatory, 168

Tantalum, 50, 51, 96, 140
  thin films, 26-28
Tapes, 76, 130
Tau Ceti, 227
Technological transfer, 117-52
Tektites, 113-14
Telemetry, 139, 165
Telephones, 122
Telescopes, 15-16, 154-80ff.
Television, 54, 163, 223
Temperature, 26-27, 34-36, 65-66
  and lunar manufacturing: See
    Manufacturing
  transportation of cold, 77
  and vacuum research: See Vacuum,
    use of
  Venusian, 177
Terrae, 81
Texas Instruments Inc., 140
Thermal Power Co., 98
Thermionic converters, 122-23
Thermistors, 139
Thermoelectric converters, 122-23
Thermonuclear fusion, 63
Thermonuclear research, 41
Thin films, 25-28, 67
Thiobacilli, 85
"This View of Life: The World
  of an Evolutionist," 209-10
Thompson-Ramo-Wooldridge, 11
Tides, 91, 106-7, 171-72, 190
"Tides, The," 106
Time, 184
Tin, 34, 51
Tiros (satellite), 169
Titan (Saturn satellite), 188
Titanium, 51, 101
Tobacco, 9
Tomato vines, 54
Torr, 18ff.
Torricelli, Evangelista, 18-19
Trans World Airlines, 146
Transducers, 124-26
Transformers, 36, 63
Transistors, 76, 140
Transition temperature, 26-27
Transmitters, 123, 139
Transportation: See Spacecraft
Tube, forming, 134
Tubes: See specific types
Tungsten, 50, 51, 53, 54, 96, 134
Tunnel diodes, 63
Turbine buckets, 137
Turbine engines, 126
Turco Products Inc., 134
Twain, Mark, 16
Twin stars and planets, 187-89
Two-dimensional circuits, 25
Tycho (crater), 112

"Ultra-cryogenic" temperatures, 34
Ultraviolet, 31, 154, 162, 174, 185
Union Carbide Corp., 139
Universe, 178-90
  See also Life, extraterrestrial;
    Planets ; etc.
Uranium, 51, 96
Uranus, 188, 189

Urey, Dr. Harold C., 14, 93, 102, 105,
  108-9, 202
  and tektites, 114
Urine, 32

Vaccines, 124, 126
Vacuum, use of, 17-44ff.
  See also specific devices, uses
Vacuum-aluminized polyester skin, 137
Vacuum tubes, 76
  See also specific types
Valves, 123
Van Allen belt, 77, 163
Van de Kamp, Dr. Peter, 196-97
Vanguard I, 122
Vega, 211
Venus, 116, 177-79, 195, 199, 212,
  217-18, 224
  twin of, 188
Verne, Jules, 68
Vibrational testing, 139
Vinyl resins, 124
Violet light, 162
Viruses, 201, 203
Vishniac, Dr. Wolf, 221
Volcanoes, 81ff., 189
Voskhod, 112
Voskhod II, 12-13
Voyager, 220

War, 119, 146-52
Water and water vapor, 47, 55-56,
  85-89, 90, 96, 104, 105, 115, 124,
  203, 212
  distilling, 32-33
  "doping" with, 26
  Martian, Venusian, 218
Weather, 123, 169-76
Webb, James E., 16
Webster, Daniel, xiv
Weightlessness, 141
Welds and welding, 30, 47, 48,
  50-51, 133-34
Westinghouse Electric Corp., 74, 140
Wheelchairs, 129-30
"When Worlds Collide," 68
Whipple, Dr. Fred L., 171
Winds, 170
"Wolftrap," 221
Wylie, Philip, 68

X-15 rocketship, 124, 133
X-20 glider, 133
X-rays, 174

Young, Stephen M., 9

Zero, absolute, 26-27
"Zero to Eighty," 68
"Zero g," 213
Zinc, 34, 51, 96, 97, 99
Zirconia, 53
Zirconium, 51, 63, 96
Zond II, 218

the author

NEIL P. RUZIC *has been championing cases for putting science to work since graduation from Northwestern University in 1950. His articles have advocated—and prophesied—such things as the emergence of advanced computers into true thinking machines, devices to keep large waterways from freezing, construction of a tunnel under the English Channel, and the concepts of management by innovation and leadership. Even before the first Sputnik he was writing articles like "Why the Race*

to Space" and "Twenty Years from Now," and stories of other worlds.

He founded Industrial Research *magazine in 1958, when he discovered "the portion of our population requiring the greatest imagination and sense of excitement, the scientists and engineers who do research, are often the most unimaginative." This book reflects one of his magazine's strong editorial policies— the hastening of space exploration.*

Prior to Industrial Research, *Ruzic was director of publications at Armour Research Foundation (now IIT Research Institute), and worked for magazines and newspapers. He majored in journalism, psychology, and science at Northwestern, is a senior member of the Institute of Electrical and Electronic Engineers, a member of Sigma Delta Chi (journalism honorary), and is listed in "Who's Who in the Midwest." He has two patent applications.*

Ruzic, now 35, has been a foreign correspondent (in Central America), a soldier, a professional photographer, and a building contractor. As president of Industrial Research Inc., he heads a company that disseminates practical scientific information through magazines, scientific brochures, and market research reports.